Gold Hits

This publication is not authorised for sale in the United States of America and/or Canada.

Wise Publications
London/New York/Paris/Sydney/Copenhagen/Madrid/Tokyo

Exclusive Distributors:
Music Sales Limited
8/9 Frith Street, London W1D 3JB, England.
Music Sales Pty Limited
120 Rothschild Avenue, Rosebery, NSW 2018, Australia.

Order No. AM963798
ISBN 0-7119-8138-8

Compiled and arranged by Stephen Duro
Music processed by Allegro Reproductions
Cover photographs courtesy of LFI and Redferns

Your Guarantee of Quality
As publishers, we strive to produce every book to the highest commercial standards.
This book has been carefully designed to minimise
awkward page turns and to make playing from it a real pleasure.
Particular care has been given to specifying acid-free, neutral-sized paper made from pulps
which have not been elemental chlorine bleached. This pulp is from farmed sustainable forests
and was produced with special regard for the environment.
Throughout, the printing and binding have been planned to ensure a sturdy, attractive publication
which should give years of enjoyment.
If your copy fails to meet our high standards, please inform us and we will gladly replace it.

All I Have To Do Is Dream

Words & Music by Boudleaux Bryant

C Bm Am D7 G
I can make you mine, Taste your lips of wine, An-y-time, night or day.
C Bm A7 D
On-ly trou-ble is, Gee whiz, I'm dream-ing my life a - way! I
G Em C D G Em C D
need you so that I could die, I love you so and that is why when
G Em C D 1. G C G
ev - er I want you all I have to do is dream.
2. G Em C D G Em C D G
dream, Dream, dream, dream, Dream, dream, dream, dream, dream.

All By Myself

Words & Music by Eric Carmen

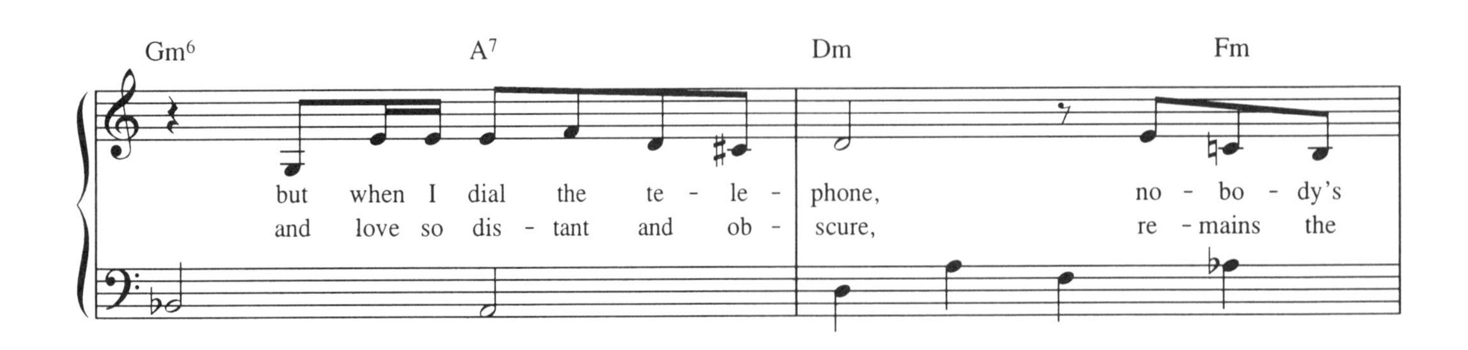

C A7 D Fm G7 C
home.
cure.
All by my -

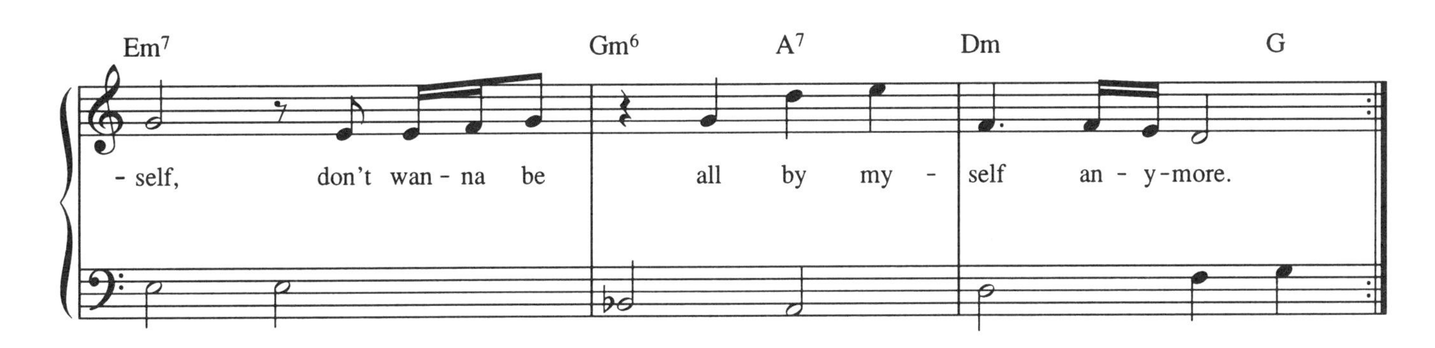
Em7 Gm6 A7 Dm G
- self, don't wan - na be all by my - self an - y-more.

C Em7 Gm6 A7
All by my - self, don't wan - na be all by my -

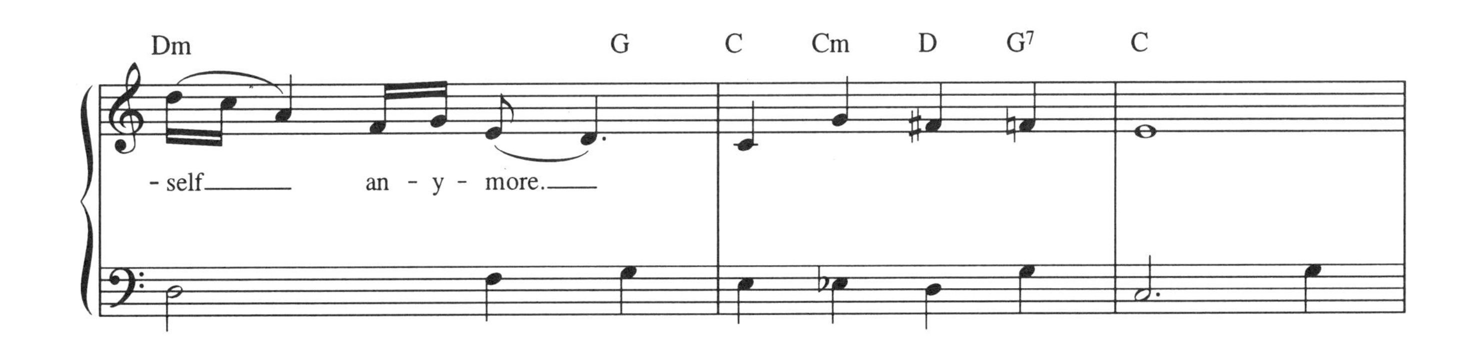
Dm G C Cm D G7 C
- self an - y - more.

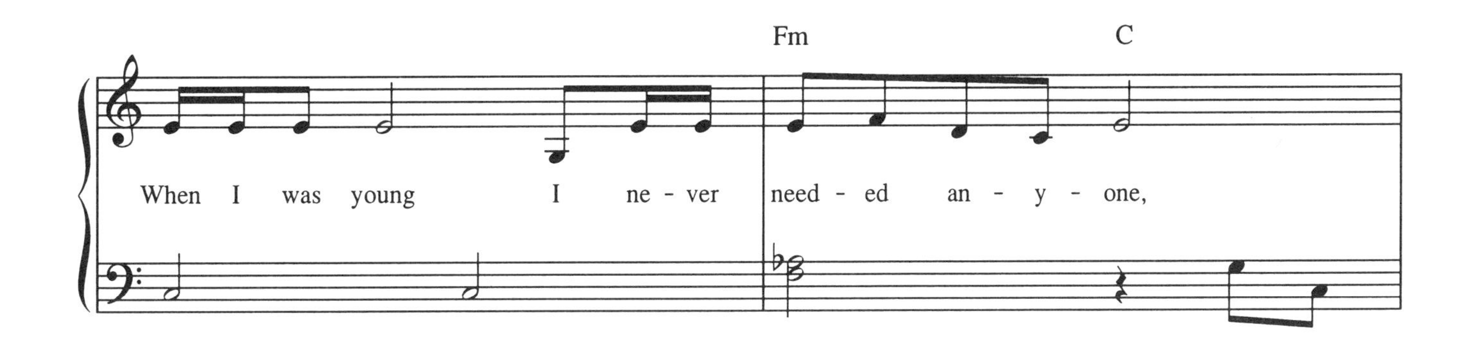
Fm C
When I was young I ne - ver need - ed an - y - one,

Gm6 A7 Dm Fm C G7
and mak-ing love was just for fun. Those days are gone.
C Em7 Gm6 A7 Dm
All by my - self, don't wan-na be all by my - self an - y -
Fm Gsus4 G C Em7 Gm6 A7
- more.
Dm G C Em7
3 3
All by my - self, don't wan - na be
Gm6 A7 Dm Fm6 G C
all by my - self an - y - more.

Big Spender

Words by Dorothy Fields
Music by Cy Coleman

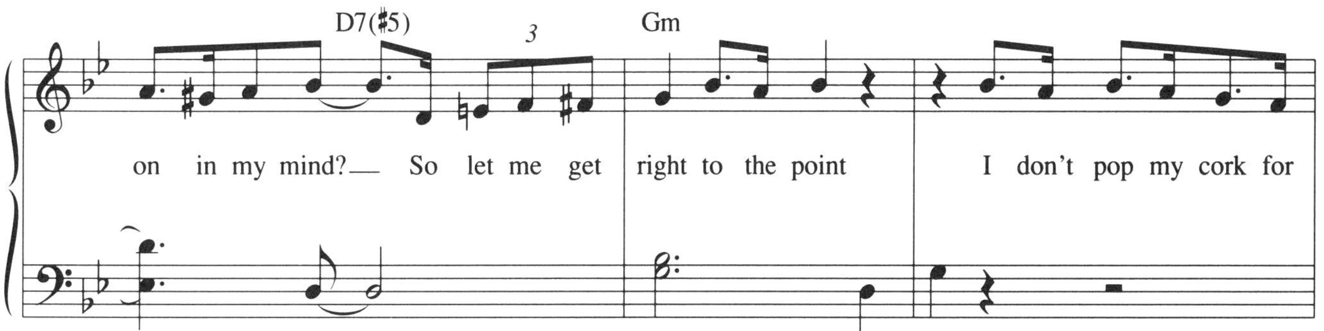

E♭
A7(♭5)
Gm
ev - ery guy I see
Hey! Big Spend - er,
To Coda
E♭7
D7
Spend
a lit - tle time with
Gm
me.
3
G
Would - n't you like to have
fun, fun,
fun? How's a - bout a few
Am
E♭9
laughs, laughs?
I can show you a
good time,

D7
E♭9
D7
D.𝄋 al Coda
3
let me show you a
good time.
The min - ute you
𝄌 Coda
A♭m
Hey Big Spend - er!
Gm
Hey, Big Spend - er!
E♭7
D7
Spend
a lit - tle time with
Gm
me.
Spend a lit - tle time with
me.
Gm9♯7
Spend a lit - tle time with
me.

Bridge Over Troubled Water

Words & Music by Paul Simon

3. Sail on silver girl, sail on by,
Your time has come to shine
All your dreams are on their way.
See how they shine.
If you need a friend
I'm sailing right behind,
Like a bridge over troubled water
I will ease your mind. (*repeat*)

Can't Help Falling In Love

Words & Music by George David Weiss, Hugo Peretti & Luigi Creatore

C D Em Am G D7 G
I can't help fall - ing in love with you.
Bm F♯7 Bm F♯7 Bm F♯7
Like a riv - er flows sure - ly to the sea, dar - ling so it goes
Bm E7 Am D7 G Bm
some things are meant to be. Take my
Em Am G D C D
hand, take my whole life too for I can't
Em Am G D7 G
help fall - ing in love with you.

Crazy

Words & Music by Willie Nelson

B♭
F
Wor - ry, why do I let my - self wor - ry;
G7
C7
Won - d'rin' what in the world did I do.
F
D7
Gm
Cra - zy for think - ing that my love could hold you.
B♭
Am
Gm
Dm
I'm cra - zy for try - in', cra - zy for cry - in' and I'm
Gm
C7
1.
F
Gm7
C7
2.
F
cra - zy for lov - in' you.
you.

Dancing Queen

Words & Music by Benny Andersson, Björn Ulvaeus & Stig Anderson

Gm F B♭
Oh, where they play the right mus - ic,
F B♭ F Gm F Gm
get - ting in the swing You come to look for a king.
B♭ E♭
A - ny - bo - dy could be that guy,
You're a teas - er you turn them on,
B♭ Gm F B♭
night is young and the mus - ic's high, with a bit of rock mus - ic
leave 'em burn - ing and then you're gone, look - ing out for an - oth - er
F B♭ F Gm F Gm
ev - ry - thing is fine. You're in the mood for a dance, and when you
an - y - one will do.

Cm7
F
B♭
E♭
get the chance,
You are the
danc-ing queen,
Young and sweet, on-ly
B♭
E♭
B♭
E♭
sev-en-teen.
Danc-ing queen,
feel the beat from the
B♭
F
E♭
F
D7
tam-bou-rine.
You can dance,
you can jive,
Gm7
C7
E♭
Cm7
hav-ing the time of your
life. Oh
see that girl,
watch that scene, dig in the
B♭
1.
E♭
B♭
E♭
2.
E♭
B♭
danc-ing queen.

Don't Cry For Me Argentina

Music by Andrew Lloyd Webber
Lyrics by Tim Rice

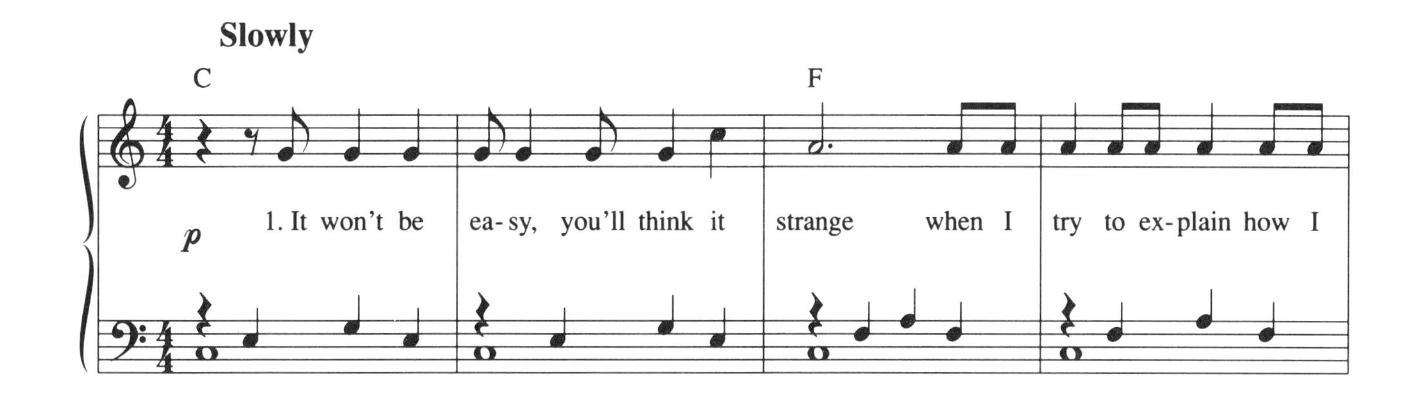

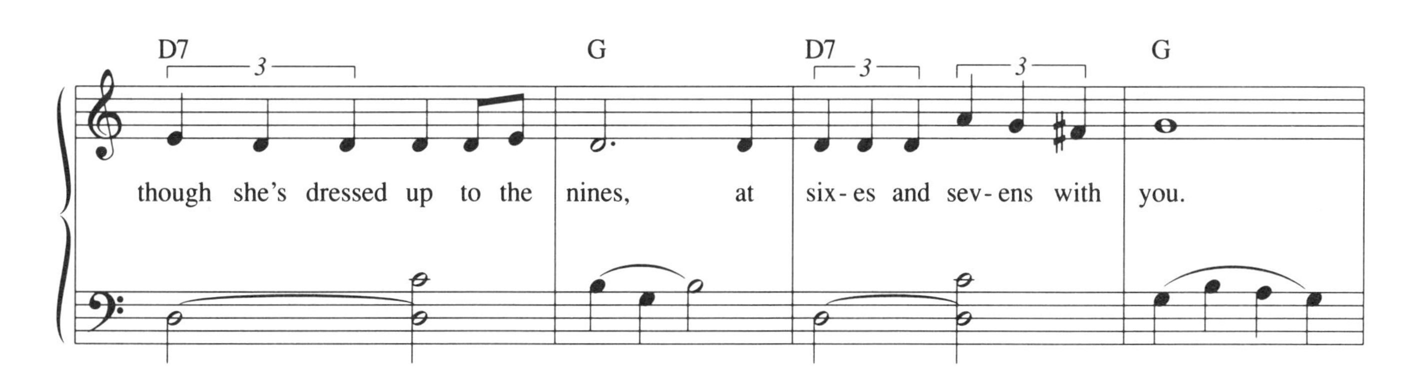

C
F
2. I had to let it hap-pen, I had to change; could-n't stay all my life down at
G/C
C
heel. Look-ing out of the win-dow, stay-ing out of the sun. So I chose
Am
D7
free - dom. Run-ning a-round try-ing ev-ery-thing new, but no-thing im-pressed me at
G
D7
G
C
all. I ne-ver ex-pect-ed it to. Don't cry for me, Ar-gen -
F
C
G
ti-na, the truth is I nev-er left you. All through my wild days, my mad ex -

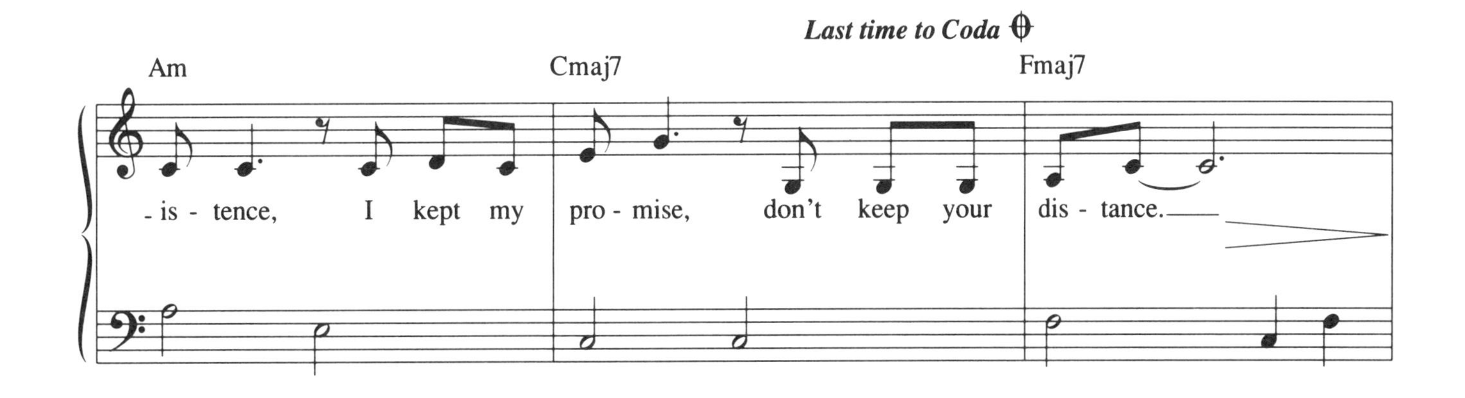

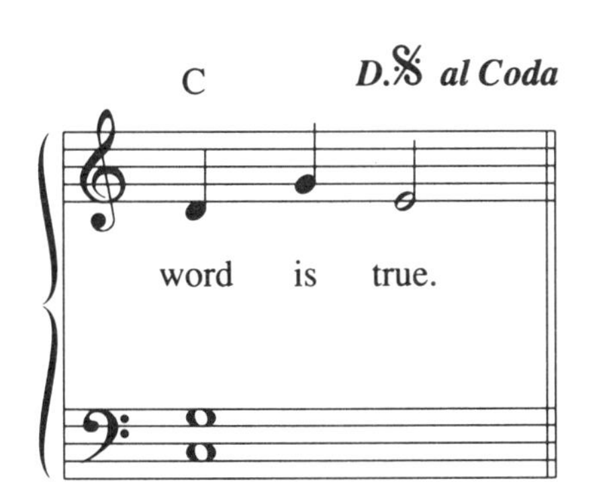

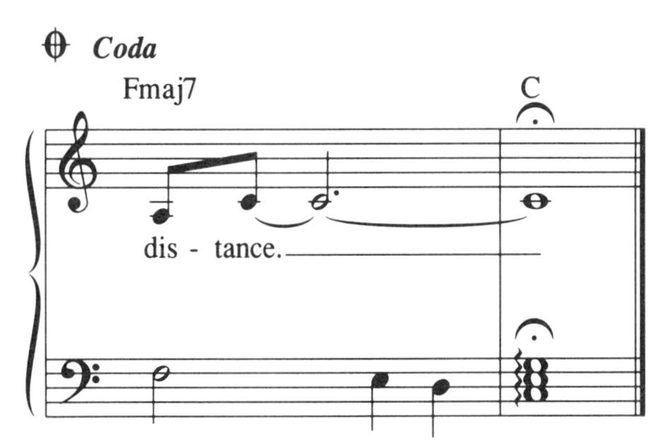

3. And as for fortune and as for fame,
I never invited them in.
Though it seemed to the world they were all I desired.
They are illusions.
They are not the solution they promised to be,
The answer was here all the time.
I love you and hope you love me.

God Only Knows

Words & Music by Brian Wilson & Tony Asher

Am
Em
A
ev - er leave me,
oh life would still go
on be - lieve me,
D
Gm
D
3
the world could show
no - thing to me,
so what good would
E
G
D
liv - ing do me?
God on - ly knows
what I'd be with - out
Em
D
G
D
you.
God on - ly knows
what I'd be with - out
Em
D
G
N.C.
D
you.
God on - ly knows.

He Ain't Heavy, He's My Brother

Words by Bob Russell
Music by Bobby Scott

G
1. Am7
2. G7
C
bro - ther.
So on we
If I'm
la - den
at
f
D7
C
D7
Bm
all,
I'm
lad - en
with
sad - ness
that
ev - 'ry - one's
Dm
Cmaj7
Em
G7
heart
is - n't
filled
with the
glad - ness
of
C
A7
Am7
D7
D.S. al Coda
love
for one an - o - ther.
It's a long, long
mf
Coda
G
Am7
G
He ain't heav - y
He's my
bro - ther.
p

Heartbeat

Words & Music by Bob Montgomery & Norman Petty

D7
C
G
D
Em
Rid-dle-dee-pat, I know that new love thrills me,
Rid-dle-dee-pat, and sing to me love's sto - ry,
D
D7
G
D7
I know that true love will be.
And bring to me love's glo - ry.
G
C
D7
Heart - beat, why do you miss when my ba - by kis - ses
Heart - beat, why do you miss when my ba - by kis - ses
G
2.
D7
G
D7
me?
me?
2.
G
D7
G

Hey Jude

Words & Music by John Lennon & Paul McCartney

1. F
2. F
F7 C7
shoul - ders.
cold - er. Da da da
da - da da da da
da.
F C Gm7 C
Hey
Jude, don't let me
down, you have
found her now go and
F B♭ F
get her. Re -
mem - ber to let her in - to your
heart, then you can
C F F
start to make it
bet - ter, bet - ter, bet - ter, bet - ter,
Oh.
Da da da
E♭ B♭ 1. F 2. F
da da da da
da da da da Hey
Jude
Jude

How Deep Is Your Love

Words & Music by Barry Gibb, Robin Gibb & Maurice Gibb

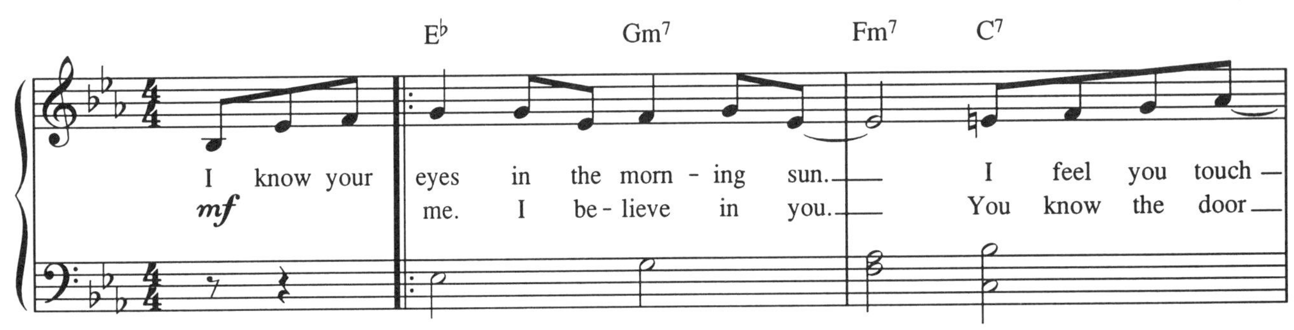

D♭9
Gm7
Fm7
- ly leave. } And it's me you need to show How deep -
- ly do.
E♭
A♭
— is your love? — How deep — is your — love? I real - ly mean — to learn,
A♭m6
E♭
B♭m
3
— 'cause we're liv - ing in a world of fools, — break - ing us
C7
Fm7
1.
A♭m6
down when they all — should let us be. — We be - long — to you — and
2.
A♭m6
E♭
Gm7
Fm7
B♭7sus4
D.S. and fade
— to you — and me. How deep —

Have I Told You Lately

Words & Music by Van Morrison

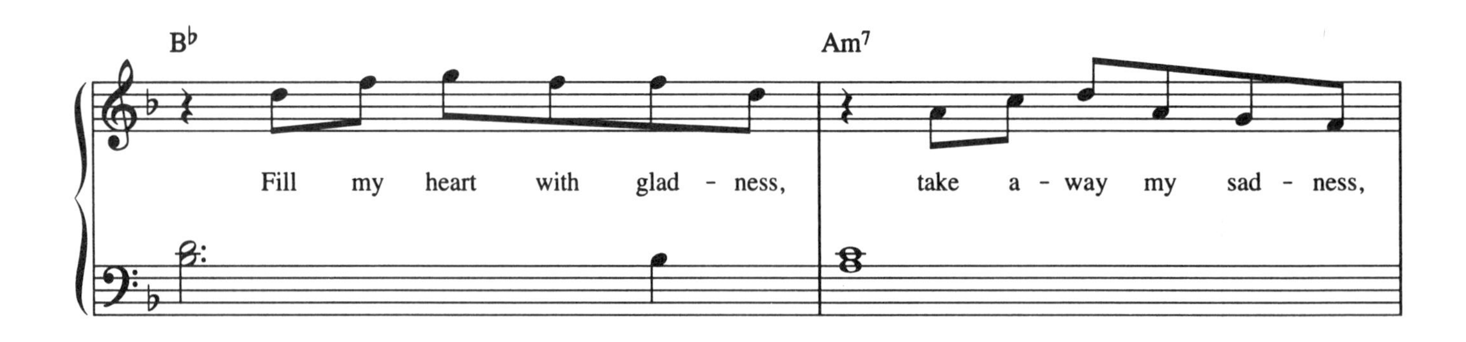

B♭
There's a love that's di-vine
And it's yours and it's mine, like the

Am
sun

B♭
3
At the end of the day
We should give thanks and pray to the

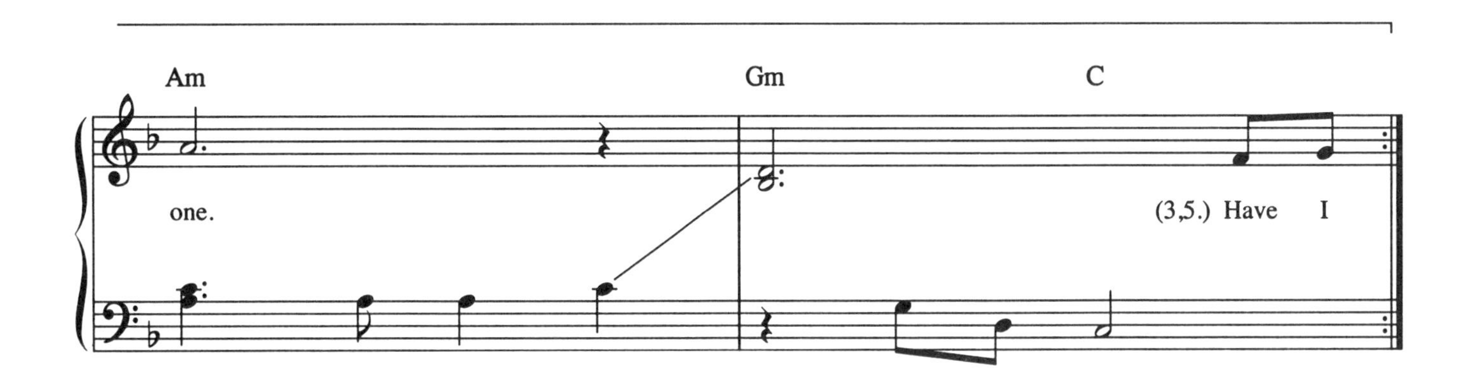
Am
Gm
C
one.
(3,5.) Have I

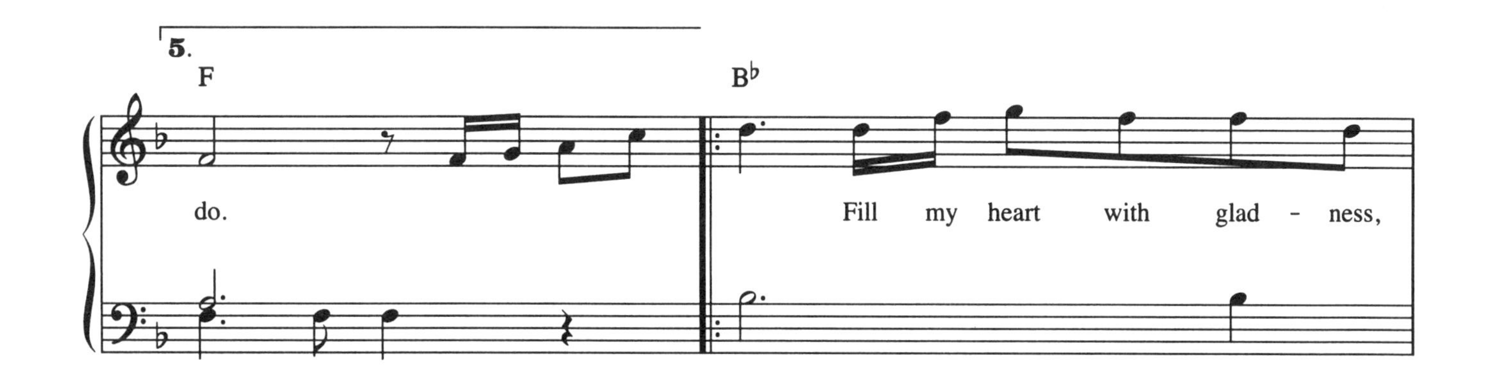

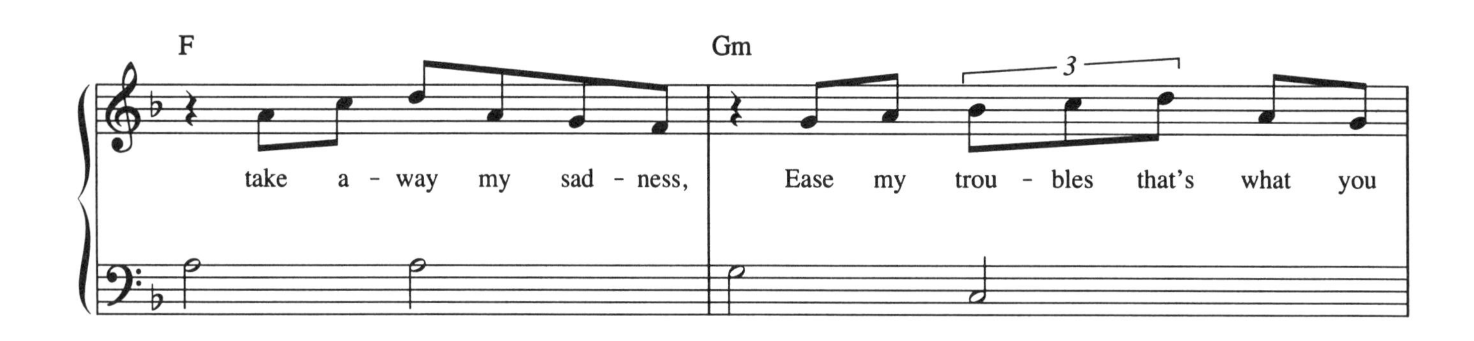

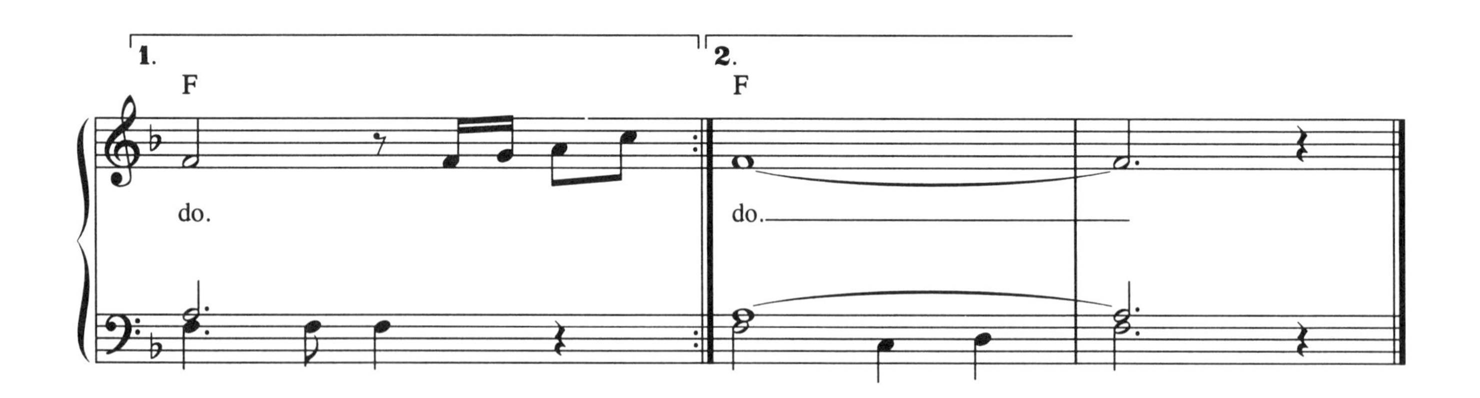

Verse 2:

Oh the morning sun in all its glory
Greets the day with hope and comfort too
And you fill my life with laughter
You can make it better
Ease my troubles that's what you do.

Middle:

There's a love that's divine
And it's yours and its mine
And it shines like the sun
At the end of the day
We will give thanks and pray to the one.

Verse 3: - as Verse 1

Verse 4: - Instrumental

Verse 5: - as Verse 1

I Believe

Words & Music by Ervin Drake, Irvin Graham, Jimmy Shirl & Al Stillman

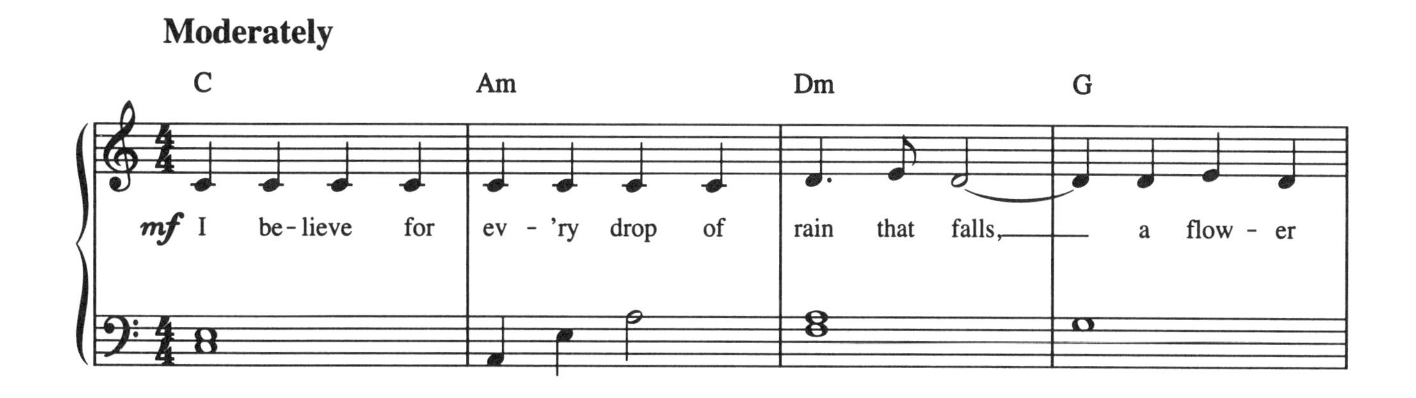

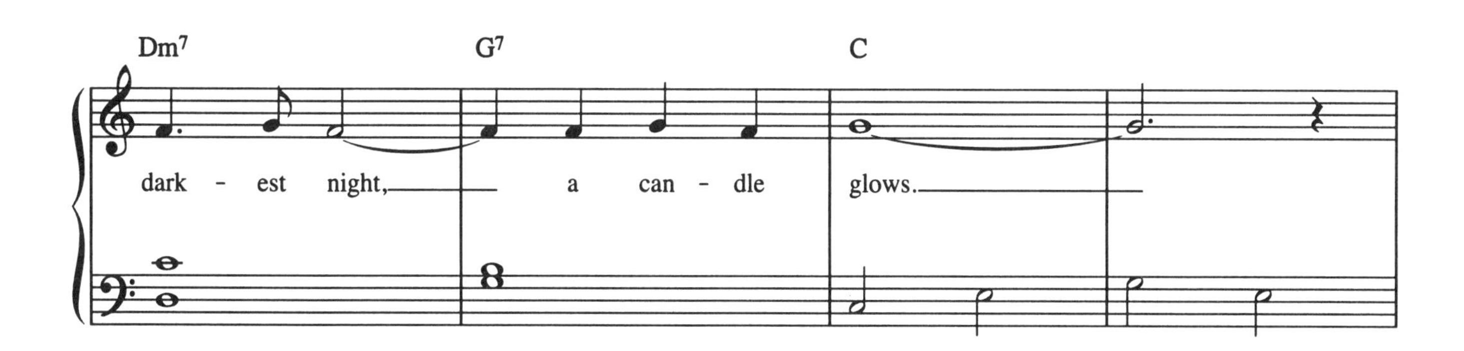

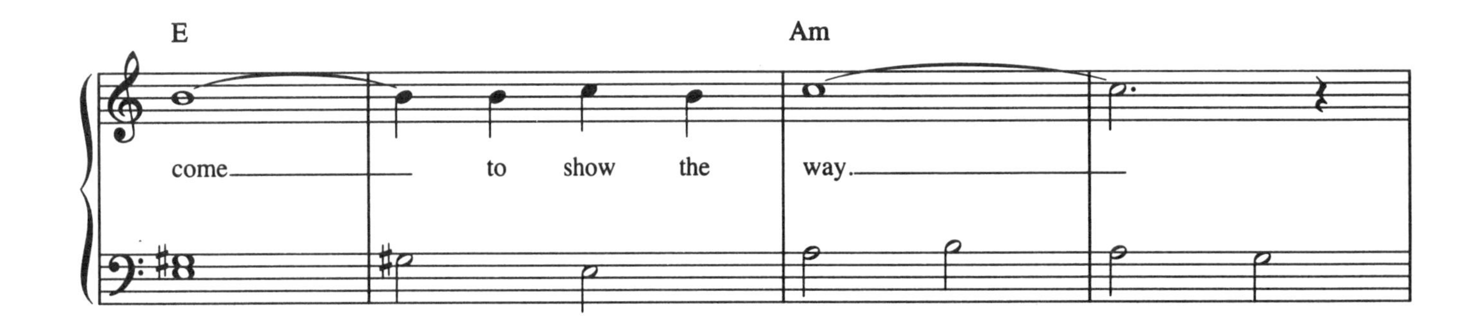
E
Am
come to show the way.

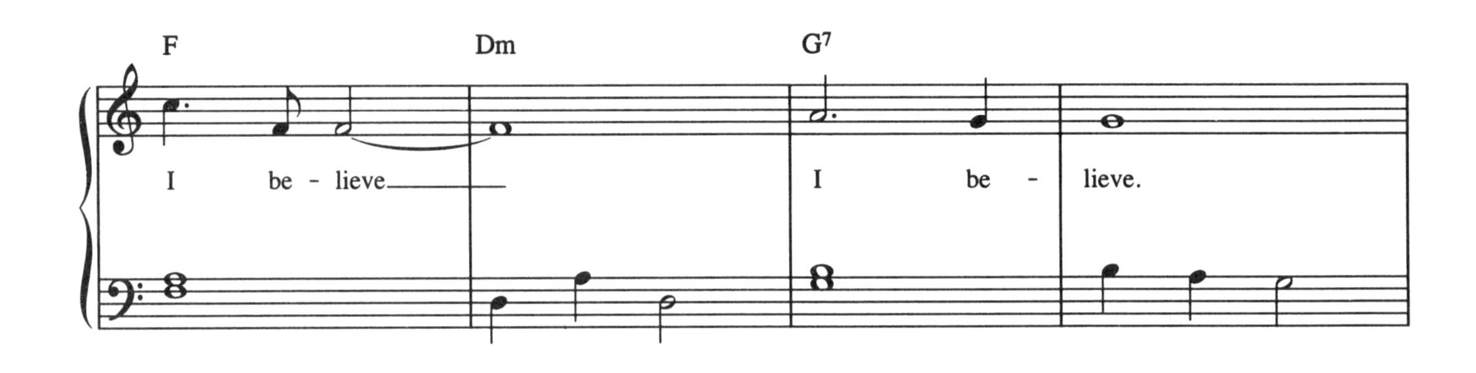
F
Dm
G7
I be - lieve I be - lieve.

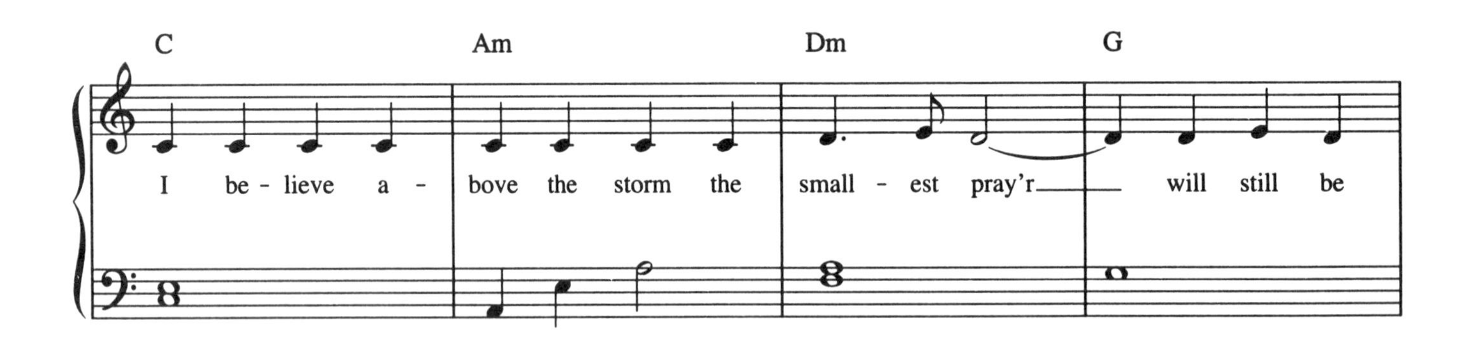
C
Am
Dm
G
I be - lieve a - bove the storm the small - est pray'r will still be

C
Am
heard. I be - lieve that some - one in the

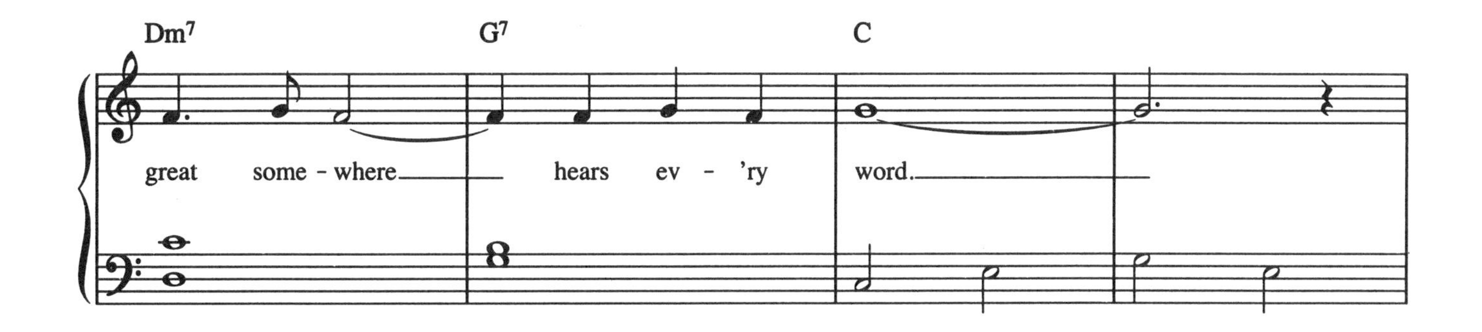
Dm7
G7
C
great some - where hears ev - 'ry word.

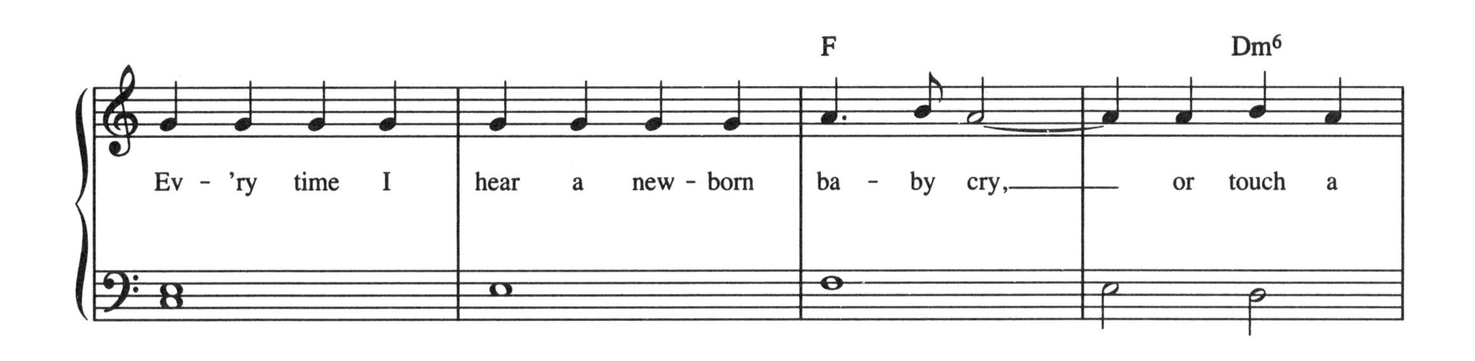
F
Dm6
Ev - 'ry time I hear a new - born ba - by cry, or touch a

E
Am
leaf, or see the sky, then I know

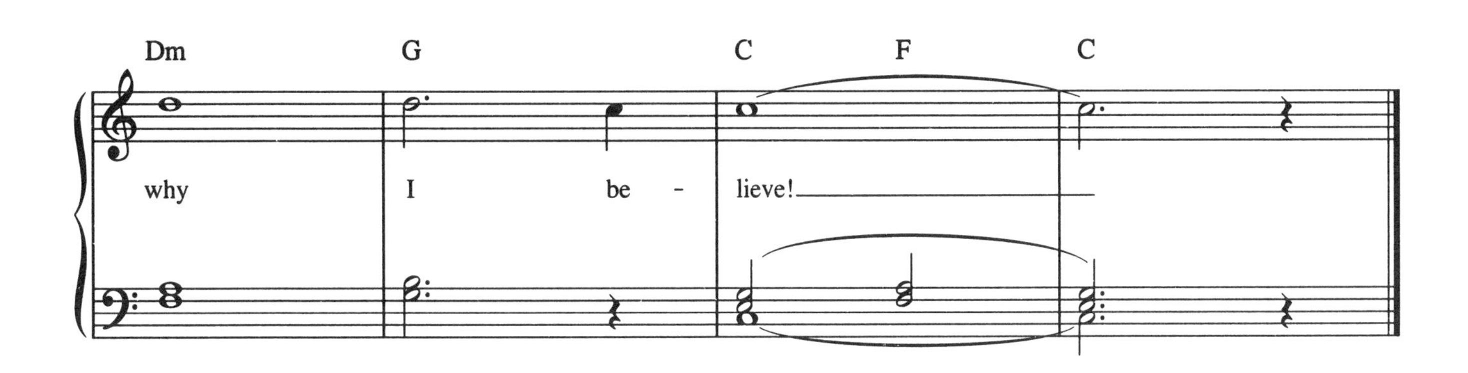
Dm
G
C
F
C
why I be - lieve!

I Say A Little Prayer

Words by Hal David
Music by Burt Bacharach

Em7
C
F
G
stay in my heart and I will love you for - ev - er and ev - er. We
Em7
C
F
G
nev - er will part. Oh, how I'll love you. To - geth - er, to - geth - er, that's
Em7
C
F
how it must be. To live with - out you would on - ly mean heart - break for
1.
E
me.
2.
E
me.
Am7
Dm7
F/G
My dar - ling be - lieve me, for me there is no one

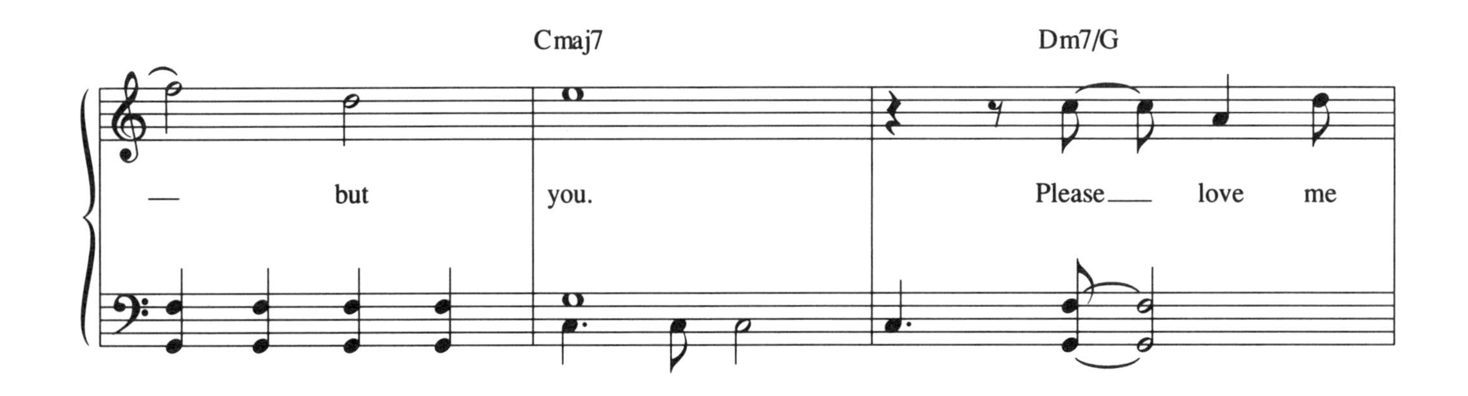
Cmaj7
Dm7/G
— but
you.
Please love me

Cmaj7
Dm7/G
C
F/G
3
too.
I'm in love with
you.
An- swer my

C
F/G
C
Dm7/G
prayer.
Say you love me
too.
dim.

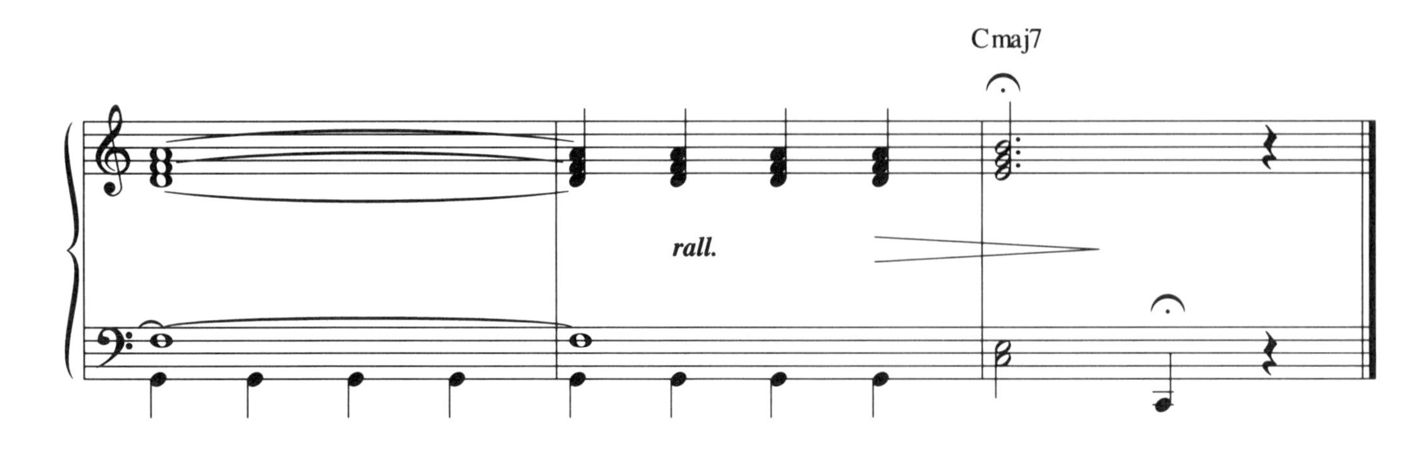
Cmaj7
rall.

I Think We're Alone Now

Words & Music by Ritchie Cordell

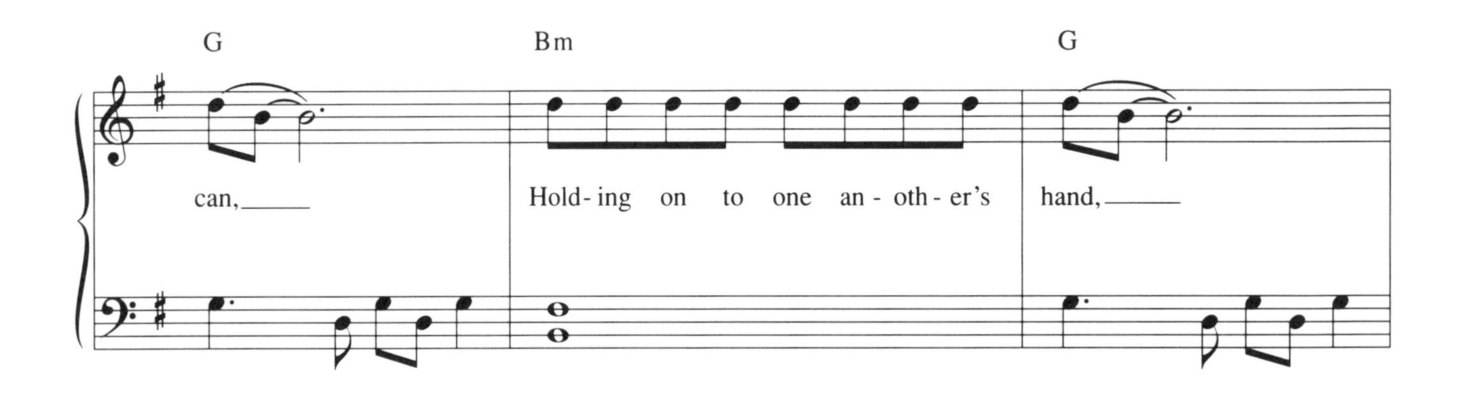
G
Bm
G
can,
Hold-ing on to one an-oth-er's
hand,

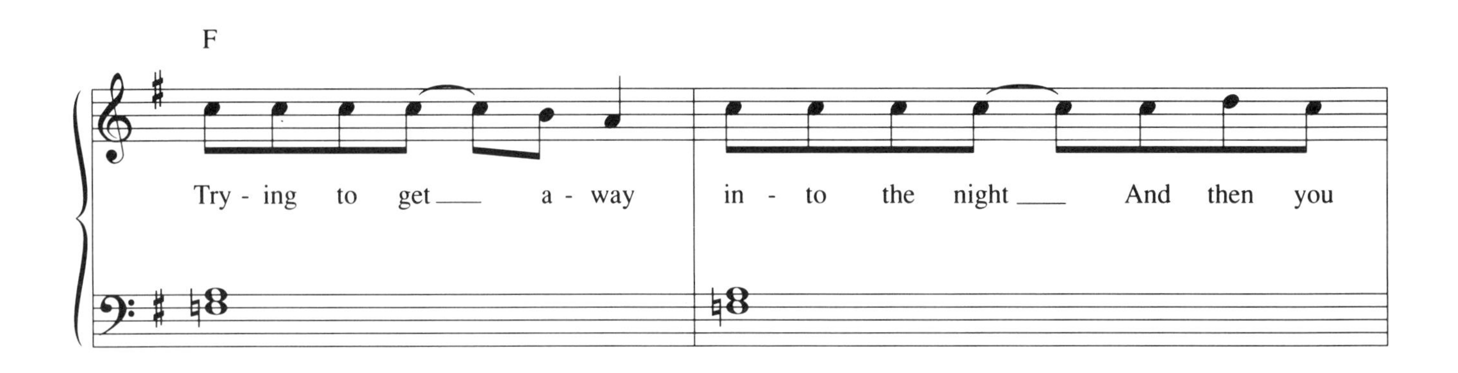
F
Try-ing to get a-way
in-to the night And then you

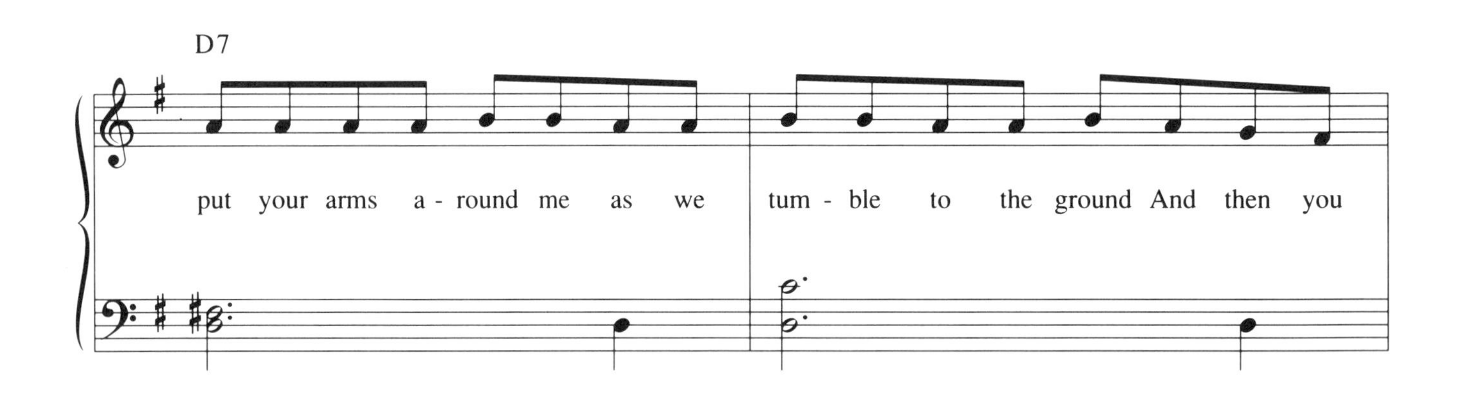
D7
put your arms a-round me as we
tum-ble to the ground And then you

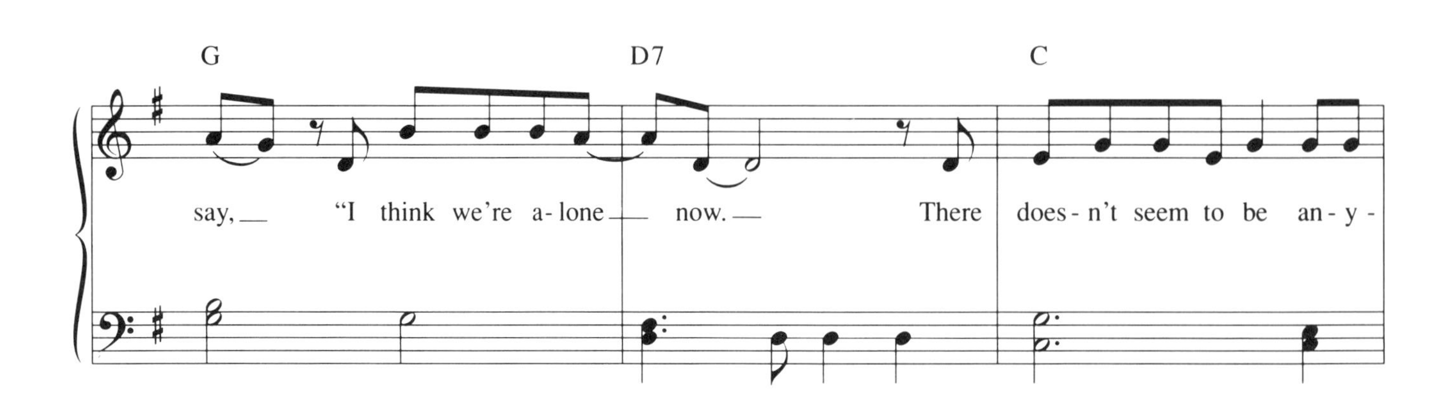
G
D7
C
say, "I think we're a-lone now.
There
does-n't seem to be an-y-

G
D7
one a - round.
I think we're a - lone now.
The

C
G
beat - ing of the hearts is the
on - ly sound."

G
D7
I think we're a - lone now.
The

C
G
beat - ing of the hearts is the
on - ly sound.

I Will Always Love You

Words & Music by Dolly Parton

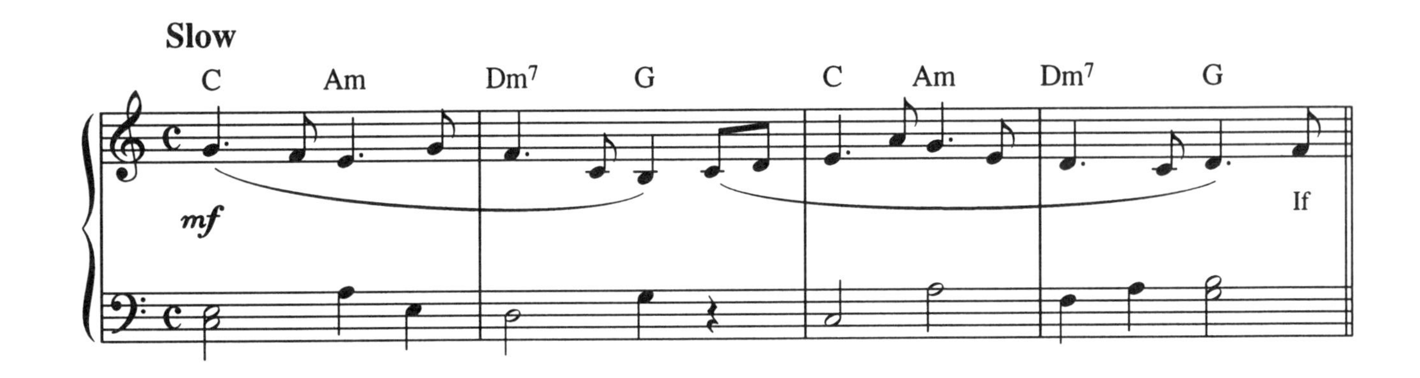

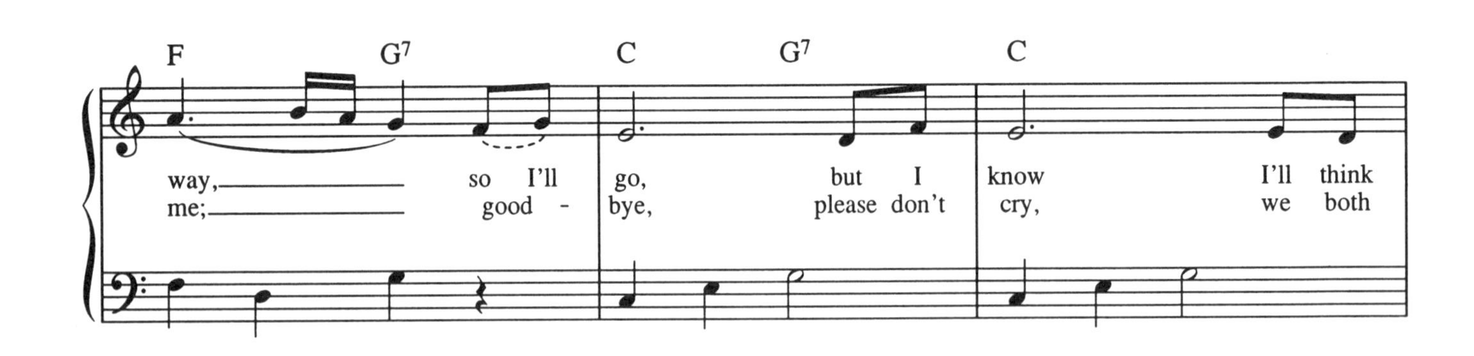

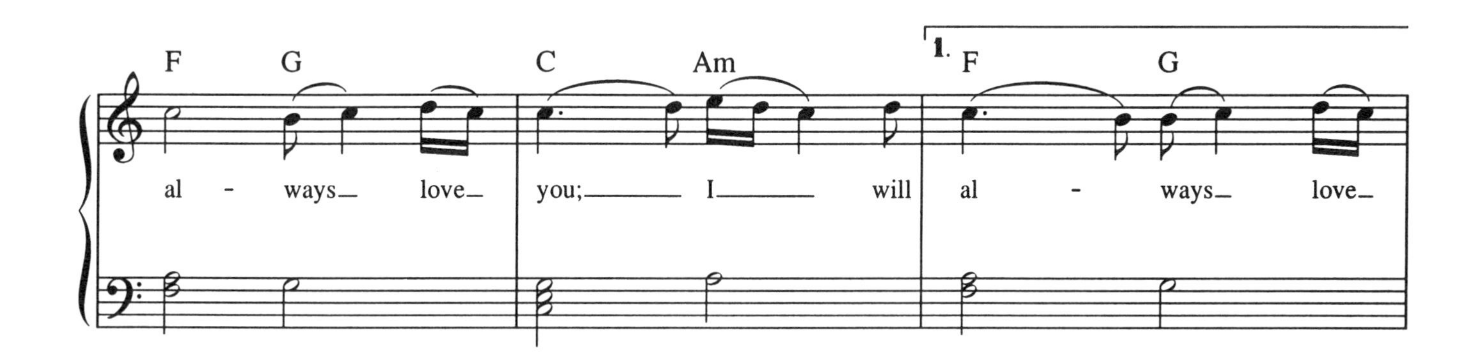

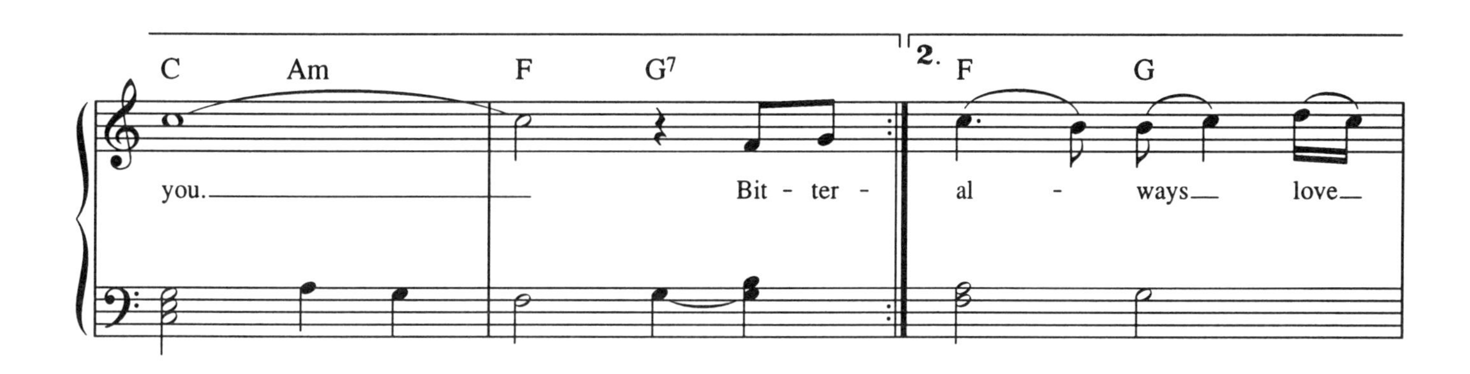

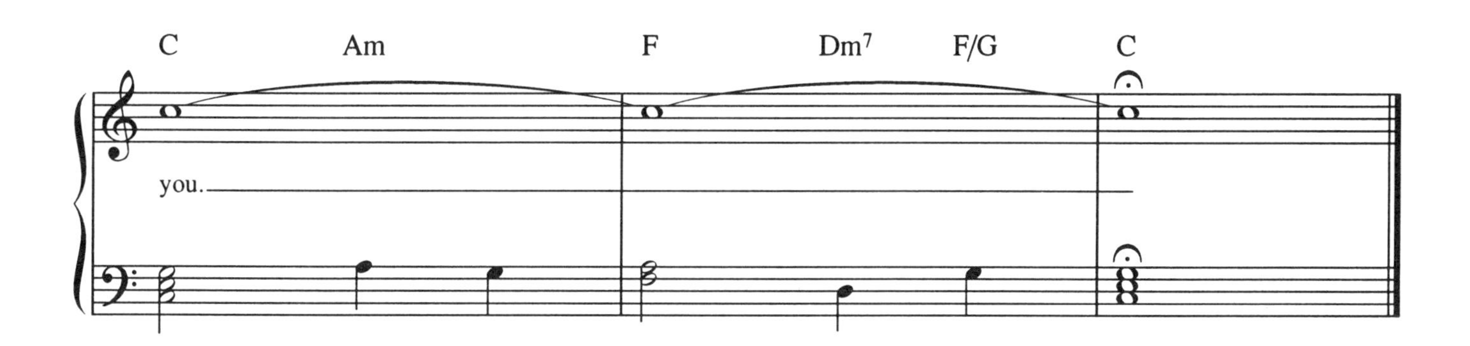

(Recited:)

I hope life treats you kind,
And I hope you have all that you ever dreamed of,
And I wish you joy and happiness,
But above all this, I wish you love.

(Sung:)

And I will always love you,
I will always love you,
I will always love you,
And I will always love you,
I will always love you,
I will always love you.

Imagine

Words & Music by John Lennon

C F C
No - thing to kill or die for And no re - li - gion
No need for greed or hun - ger A broth - er - hood of
F Am Dm7
too I - ma - gine all the peo - ple
man I - ma - gine all the peo - ple
G F G
Liv - ing life in peace yu - huh You may say I'm a
Shar - ing all the world yu - huh
C E F G C E F G
dream - er But I'm not the on - ly one I hope some day you'll
C E F G 1. C 2. C
join us And the world will be one. live as one.

In The Air Tonight

Words & Music by Phil Collins

C/D
B♭/D
would not lend a hand I've seen your face be-fore, my
how could I ev-er for-get, it's the first time
Dm
friend, but I don't know if you know who I am. Well,
the last time we ev - er met. But I
C/D
I was there and I saw what you did, I saw it with my own two eyes
know the reas-on why you keep the sil - ence up No you don't fool
B♭/D
so you can wipe off that grin I know where you've been it's
me The hurt does-n't show but the pain still grows, it's no
Dm
1.
2.
D.𝄋 al Coda
all been a pack of lies.
stran - ger to you or me.

Coda
Dm C/D B♭/D
I can feel it in the air to-night oh Lord oh Lord
C/D Dm C/D
Well, I've been wait-ing for this mo-ment for all my life
B♭/D C/D Dm C/D
oh Lord. and I can feel it com-ing in the air to-night
B♭/D C/D Dm
oh Lord, Well, I've been wait-ing for this
C/D B♭/D C/D Dm
mom-ent for all my life oh Lord.

Killing Me Softly With His Song

Words by Norman Gimbel
Music by Charles Fox

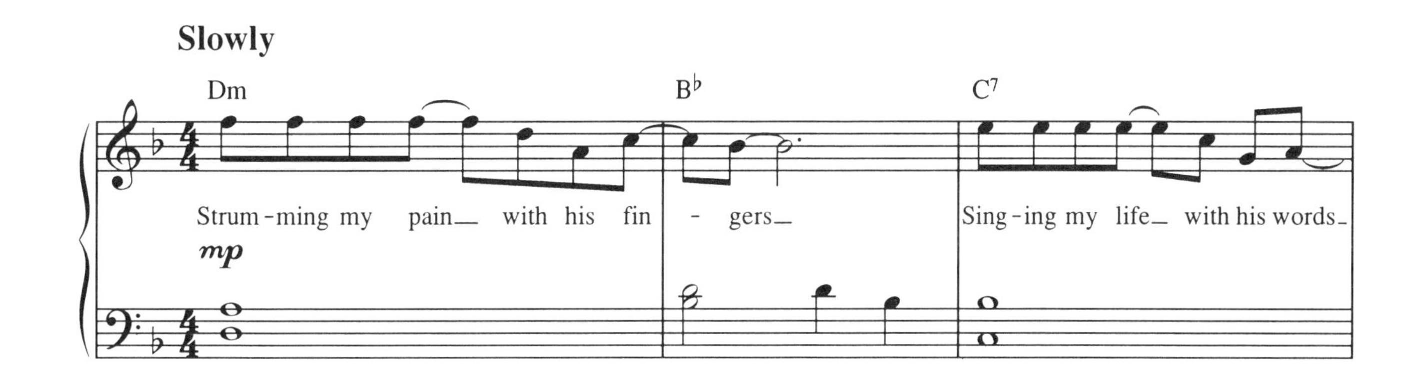

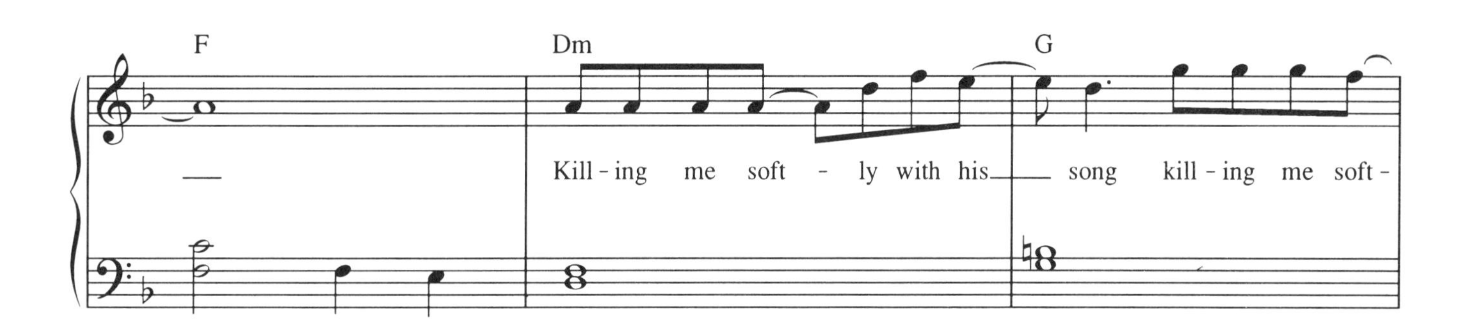

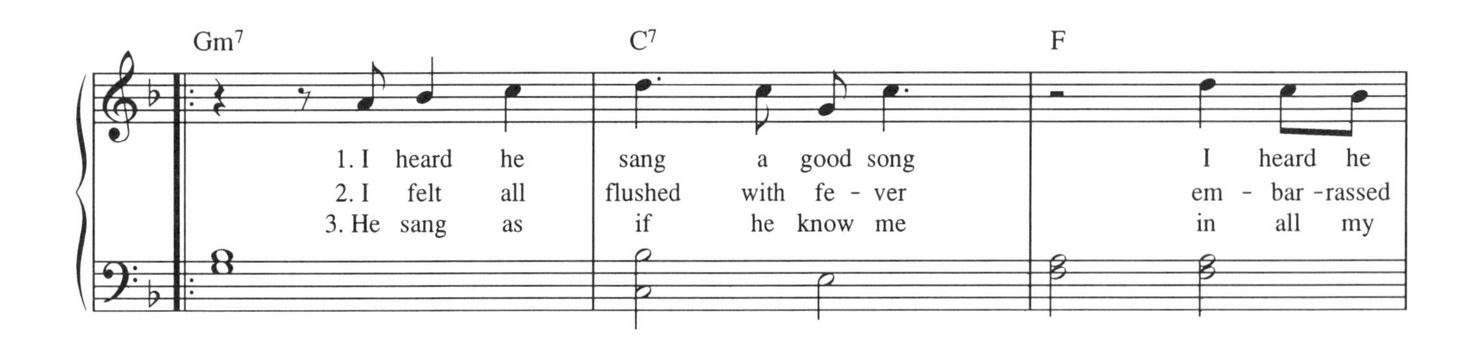
Gm7
C7
F
1. I heard he sang a good song I heard he
2. I felt all flushed with fe - ver em - bar - rassed
3. He sang as if he know me in all my

B♭
Gm7
C7
had a style And so I came to see him and
by the crowd I felt he found my let - ters and
dark des - pair And then he looked right through me as

Dm
Gm7
lis - ten for a while And there he was
read each one out loud I prayed that he
if I was - n't there But he was there

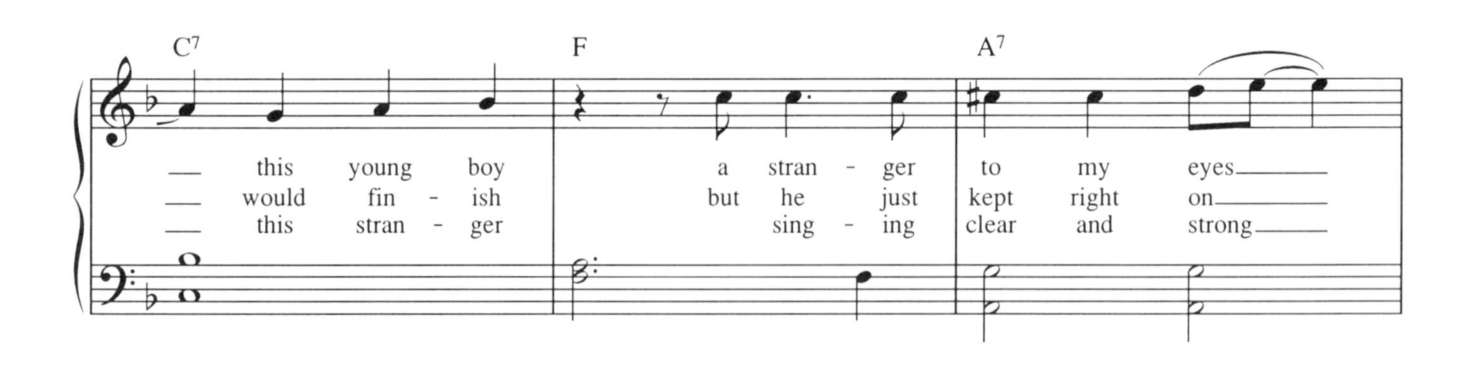
C7
F
A7
this young boy a stran - ger to my eyes
would fin - ish but he just kept right on
this stran - ger sing - ing clear and strong

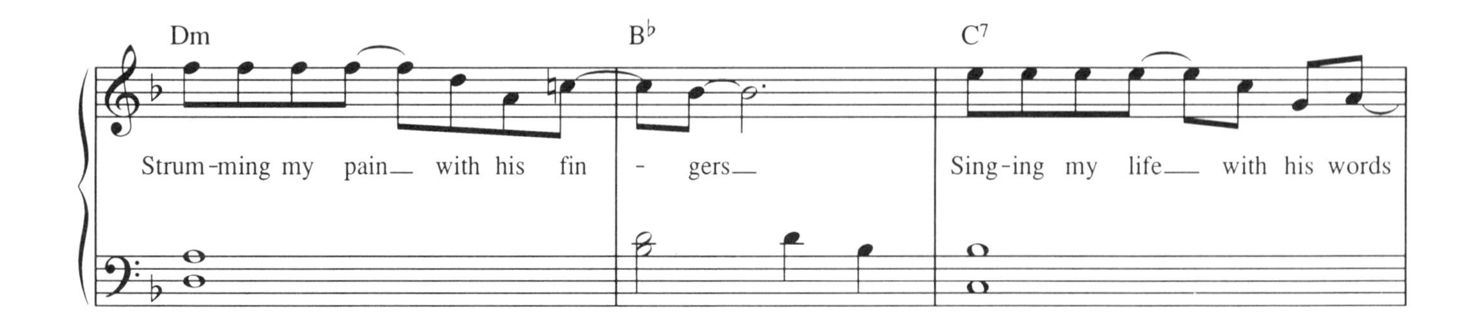
Dm
B♭
C7
Strum-ming my pain with his fin - gers
Sing-ing my life with his words

F
Dm
G
kill - ing me soft - ly with his song kill - ing me soft -

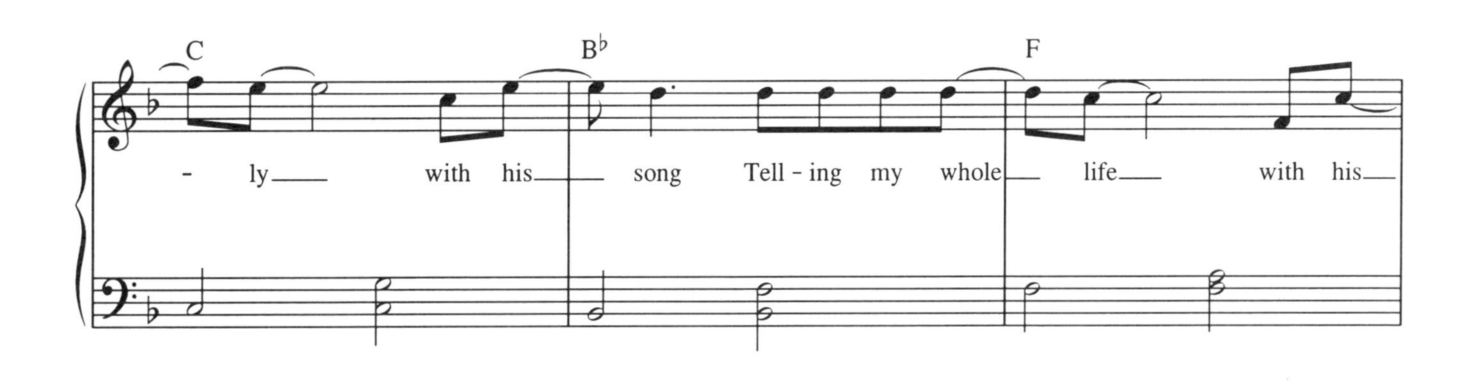
C
B♭
F
- ly with his song Tell - ing my whole life with his

B♭
Dm
Dsus4
words kill - ing me soft - ly with his

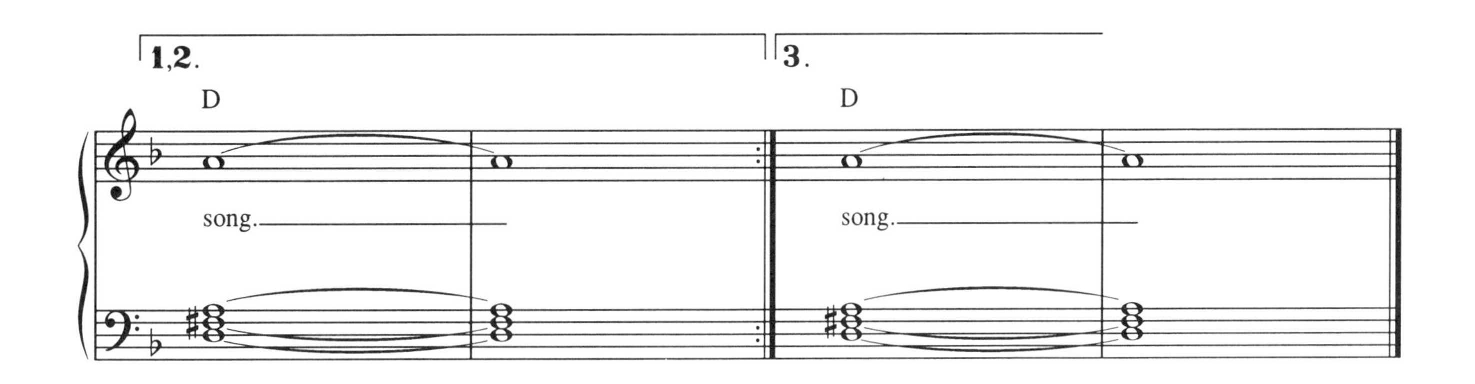
1,2.
3.
D
D
song.
song.

Moon River

Words by Johnny Mercer
Music by Henry Mancini

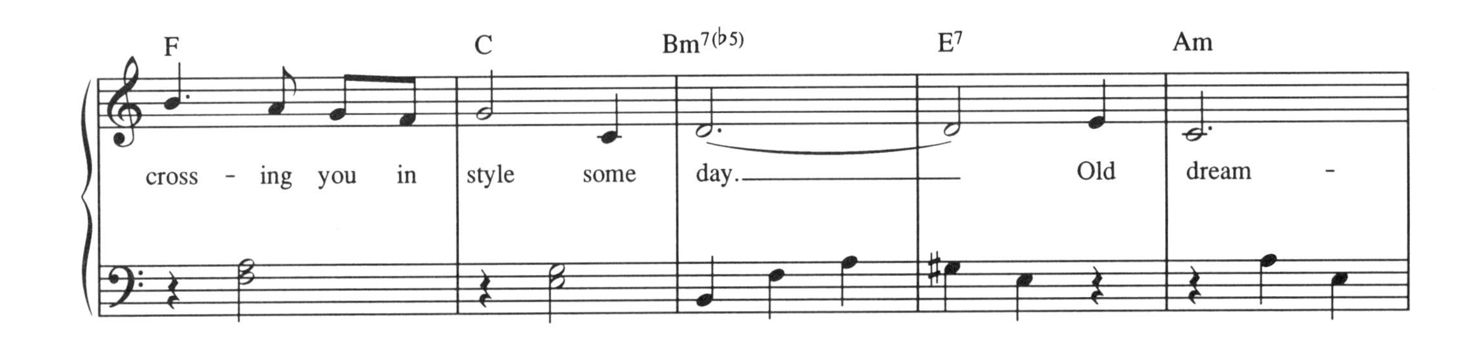

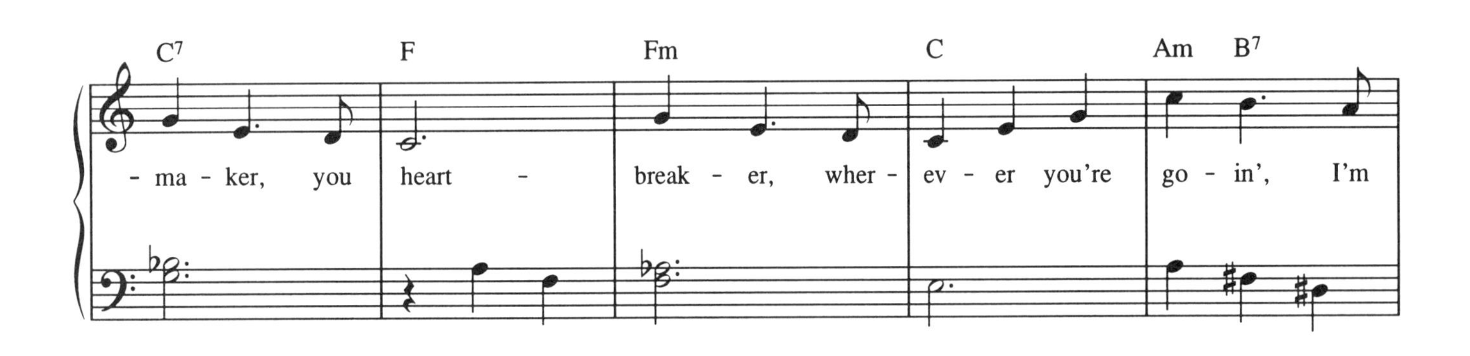

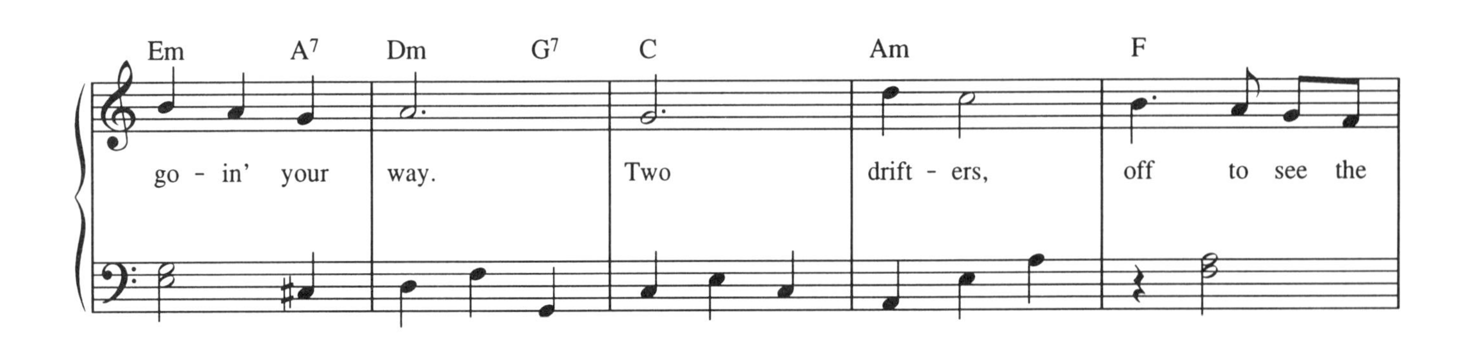

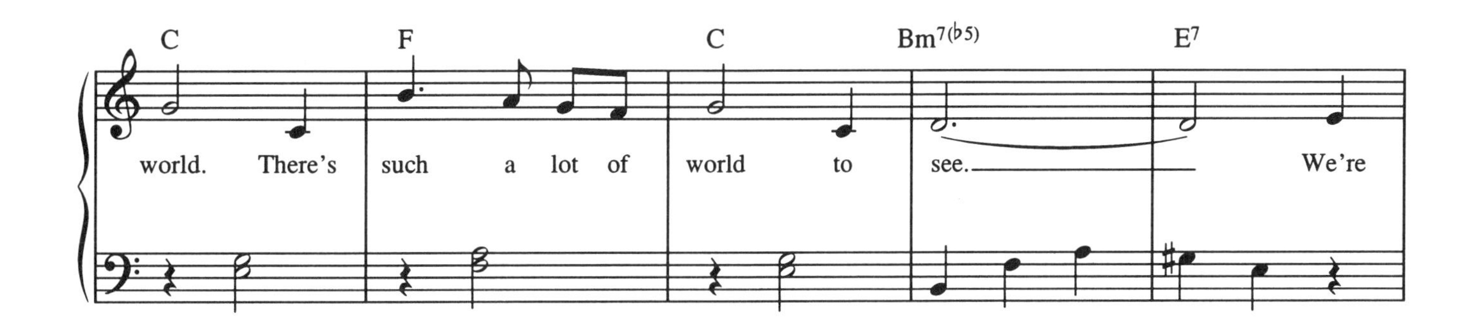
C
F
C
Bm7(♭5)
E7
world. There's such a lot of world to see. We're

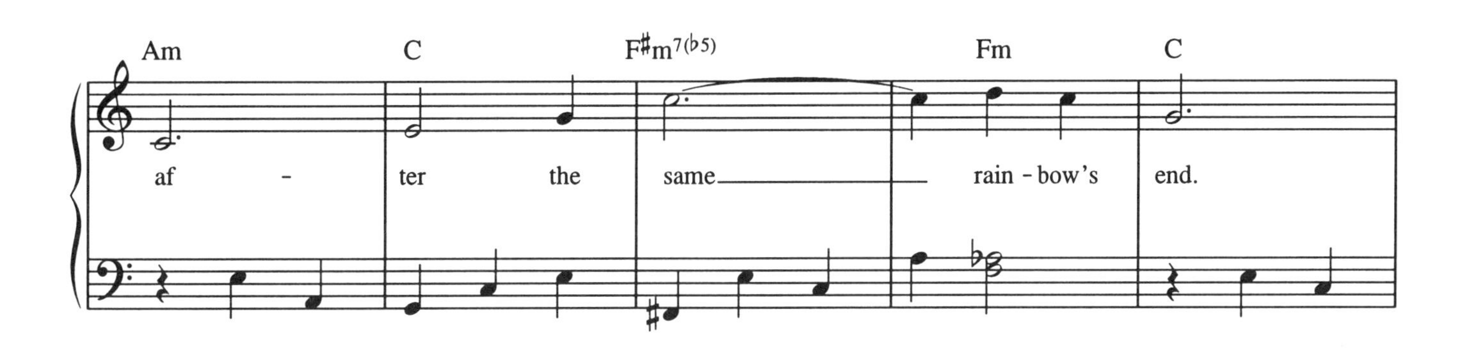
Am
C
F♯m7(♭5)
Fm
C
af - ter the same rain - bow's end.

F
C
F
C
Am
wait-in' round the bend, My huck-le-ber-ry friend, Moon

Dm7
G7
F
D♭maj7
C
ri - ver and me.

Only The Lonely

Words & Music by Roy Orbison & Joe Melson

C
They're gone for - ev - er
So far a -
No more sor - row
But that's the
A7
D7
G
part
But on - ly the
lone - ly
chance
You've got to take
if you're
G7
C
know
why
I
lone - ly
Heart -
D7
1.
G
cry
on - ly the
lone - ly.
break
on - ly the
2.
G
On - ly the
lone - ly.

The Power Of Love

**Words & Music by Candy de Rouge, Gunther Mende,
Jennifer Rush & Susan Applegate**

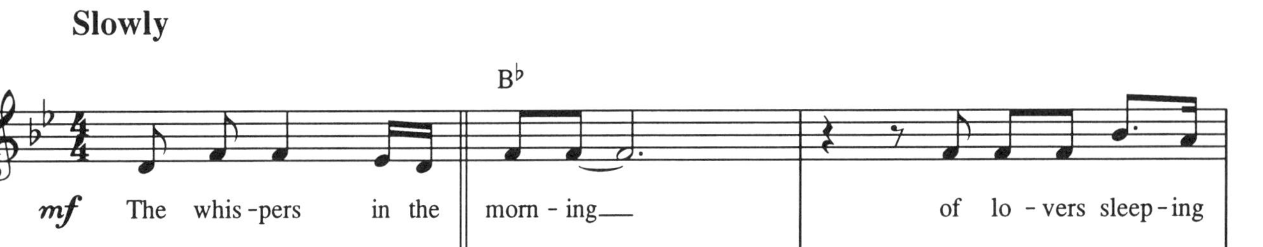

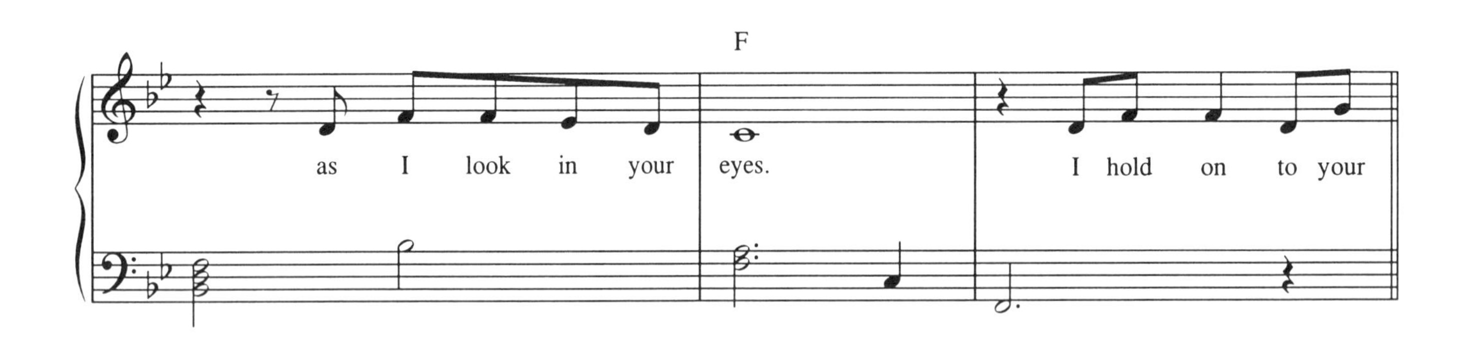

E♭
Your voice is warm and ten - der, a love that
But ne - ver won - der where I am 'cause I am
B♭
F
I could not for - sake.
al - ways by your side.
'Cause I am your la -
B♭
E♭
- dy and you are my man.
Cm
When - ev - er you reach for me
I'm gon - na do all that I can.
F
1.
F7
Ev - en though there may be
2.
F7
We're head - ing for

B♭
E♭
some - thing,
Some - where I've ne - ver
been,

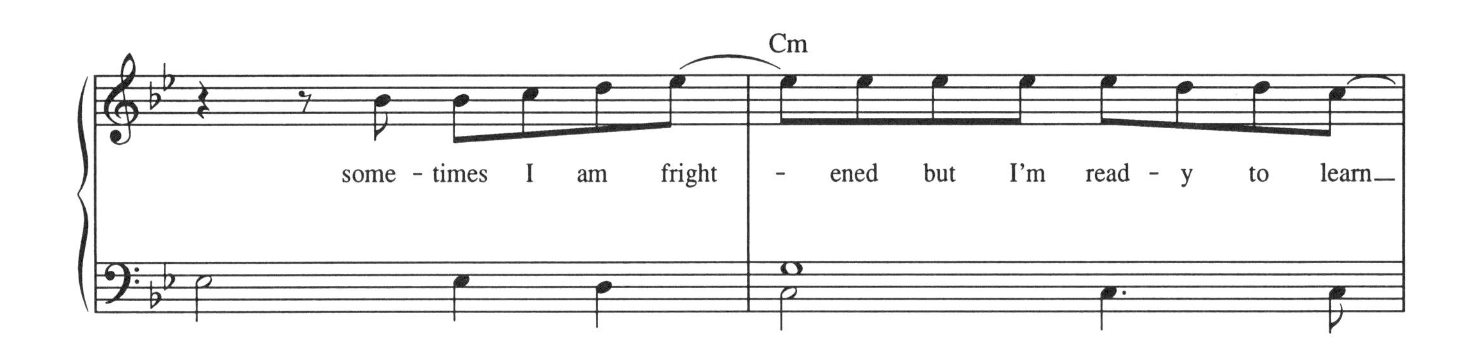
Cm
some - times I am fright - ened but I'm read - y to learn

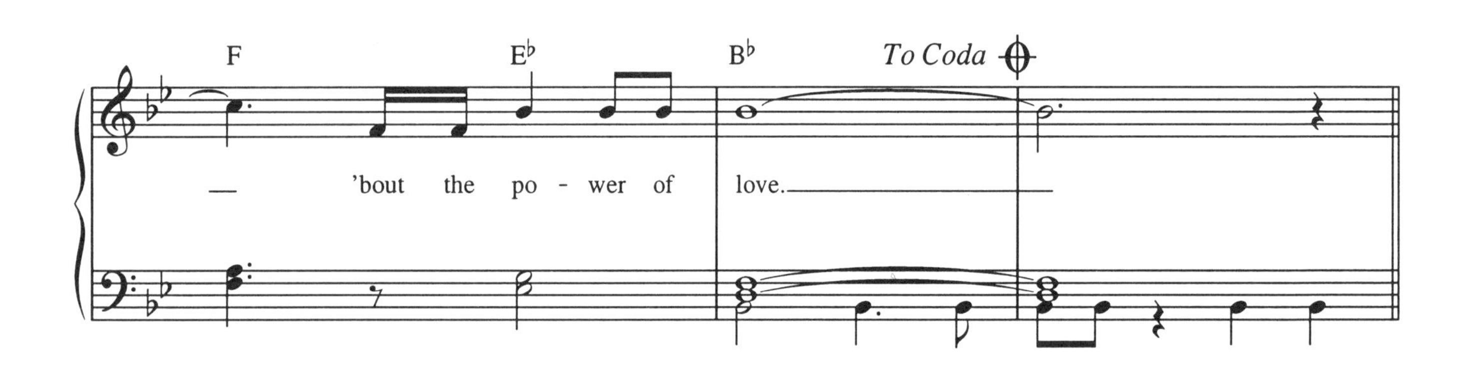
F
E♭
B♭
To Coda
'bout the po - wer of
love.

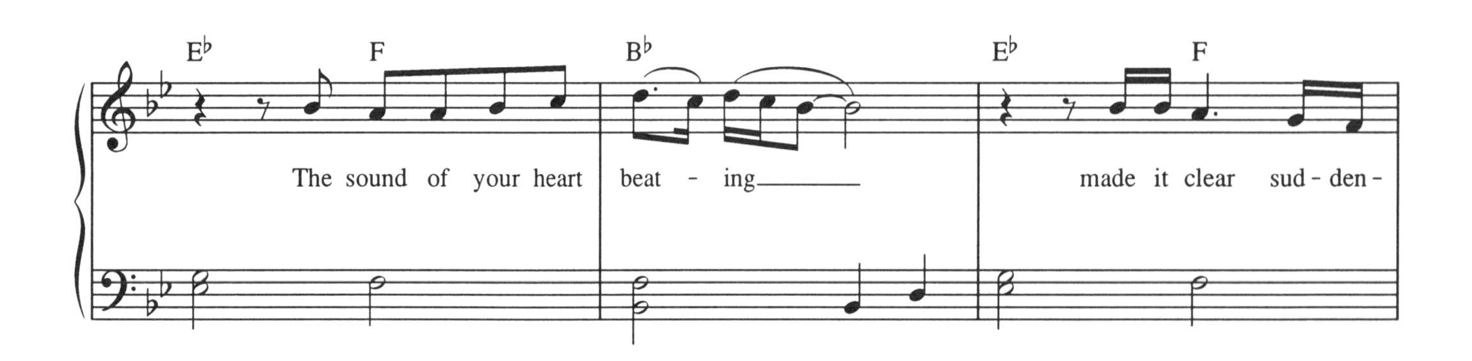
E♭
F
B♭
E♭
F
The sound of your heart
beat - ing
made it clear sud - den -

Gm
E♭
F
B♭
- ly.
The feel - ing that I
can't go on

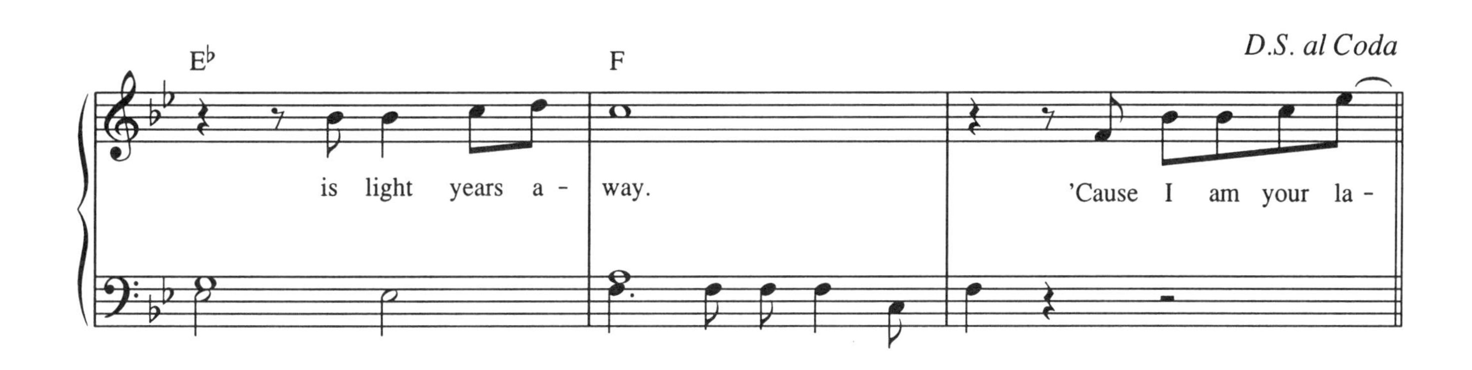
E♭
F
D.S. al Coda
is light years a -
way.
'Cause I am your la -

CODA
The po-wer of love.
The po-wer of love.

E♭
B♭
The po - wer of love.

Rocket Man

Words & Music by Elton John & Bernie Taupin

Em7
A7
C
G
it's lone-ly out in space,
on such a time
Am
D
Am7/D
- less flight.
G
And I think it's gon - na be a long long time
C
'til touch - down brings me round a - gain to find
G
C
G
I'm not the man they think I am at home, Oh no no no, I'm a

A7
C
rock - et man.
Rock - et man
burn - ing out his fuse up here
G
C
To Coda
1.
2.
a - lone.
Em7
A7
Mars ain't the kind of place to
raise your kids,
Em7
A7
C
G
In fact it's cold as
hell.
And there's no one there to
raise
Am
D
them
if you did.

Em7
A7
And all this sci - ence I don't un - der - stand.
Em7
A7
C
G
It's just my job five days a week. A rock - et man,
D.𝄋 al Coda
Am7
D
Am7/D
A rock - et man.
CODA
C
G
And I think it's gon - na be a long, long time.
C
G
And I think it's gon - na be a long, long time.

Romeo And Juliet

Words & Music by Mark Knopfler

C
D
To Coda
You and me babe how a - bout it?
G
D
Em
D
(Spoken): Juliet says, hey, it's Romeo, you nearly gave me a heart attack.
G
Bm7
Em
C
(Sung): He's un- der- neath the win- dow, she's sing- ing, hey la my boy- friend's back.
D
C
D
3
G
You should- n't come a- round here, sing- ing up at peo- ple like that
C
Dsus4
D
an - y - way, what you gon - na do a - bout it? Ju- li -

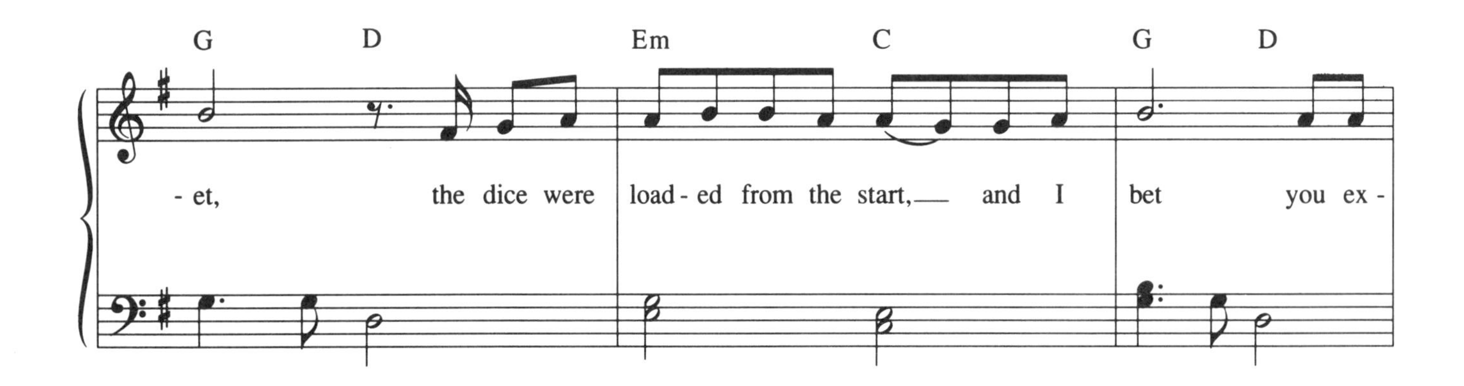
G
D
Em
C
G
D
- et, the dice were load - ed from the start, and I bet you ex -

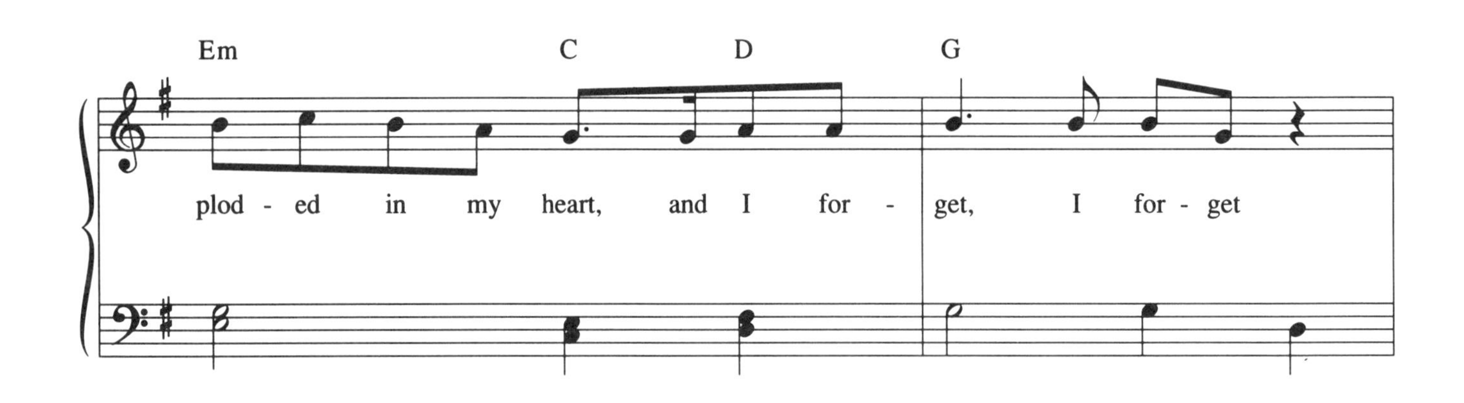
Em
C
D
G
plod - ed in my heart, and I for - get, I for - get

Em
C
Am
G
the mov - ie song, When you gon - na re - a - lise it was

C
Em
C
G
D
C
D
just that the time was wrong, Ju - li - et?

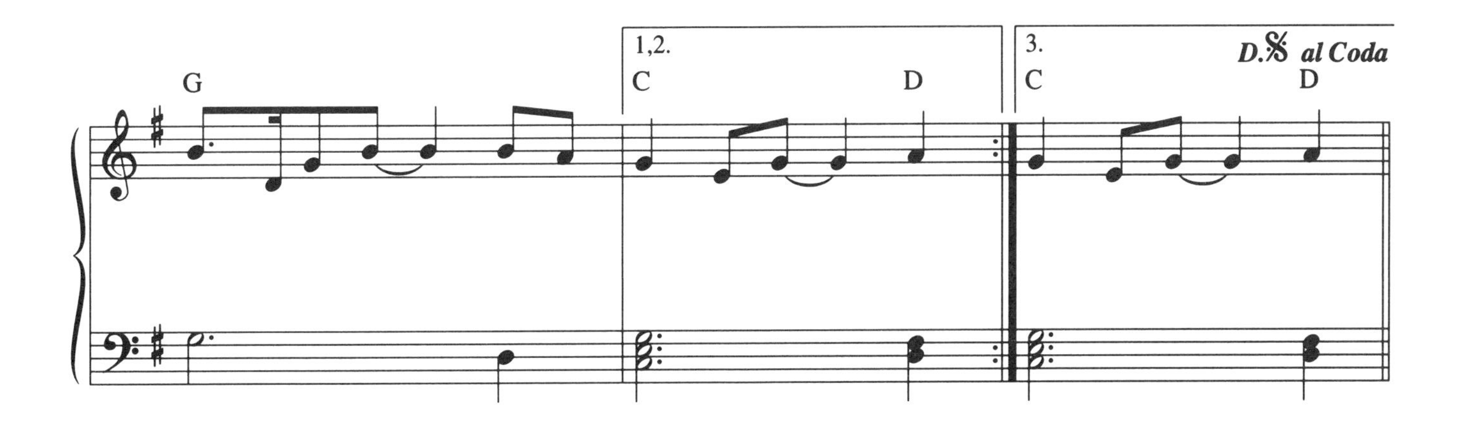

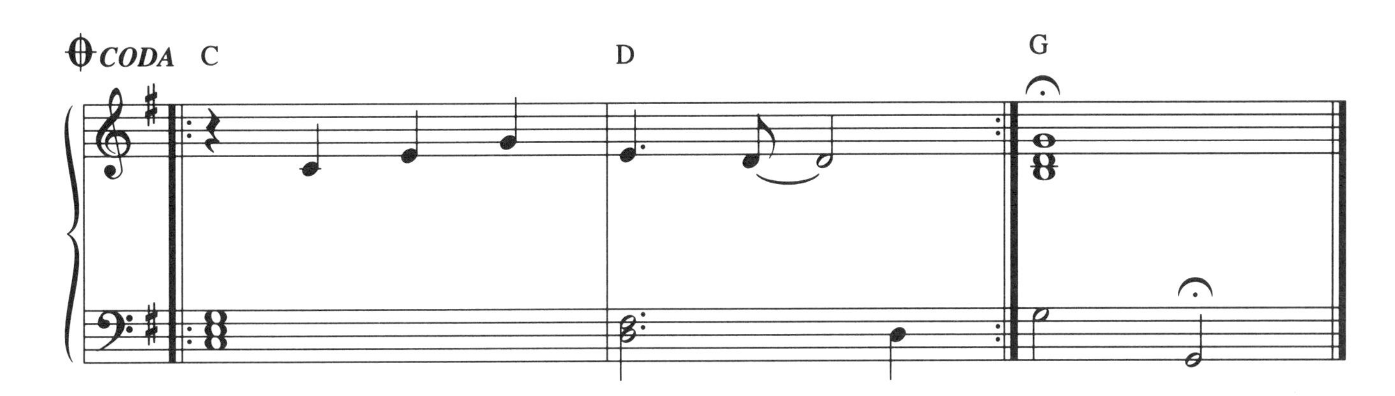

VERSE 2:
Come up on different streets
They both were streets of shame.
Both dirty, both mean,
Yes and the dream was just the same.
And I dreamed your dream for you
And now your dream is real.
How can you look at me
As if I was just another one of your deals.

When you can fall for chains of silver
You can fall for chains of gold
You can fall for pretty strangers
And the promises they hold.
You promised me everything,
You promised me thick and thin
Now you just say oh Romeo, yeah,
You know I used to have a scene with him.

CHORUS 2:
Juliet, when we made love you used to cry
You said I love you like the stars above,
I'll love you 'til I die.
There's a place for us
You know the movie song,
When you gonna realise
It was just that the time was wrong,
Juliet?

VERSE 3:
I can't do the talk
Like they talk on T.V.
And I can't do a love song
Like the way it's meant to be.
I can't do everything
But I'd do anything for you
I can't do anything
Except be in love with you.

And all I do is miss you
And the way we used to be
All I do is keep the beat
And bad company.
All I do is kiss you
Through the bars of a rhyme
Julie I'd do the stars
With you any time.

CHORUS 3:
Juliet, when we made love you used to cry
You said I love you like the stars above,
I'll love you 'til I die.
And there's a place for us
You know the movie song,
When you gonna realise
It was just that the time was wrong,
Juliet?

Nights In White Satin

Words & Music by Justin Hayward

A
C
love you, Yes, I love you, oh how I
love you, Yes, I love you, oh how I
Em
D
1. Em
D
love you.
love you.
2.3. Em
D
To Coda
Em
How I love you.
Em
D
C
B
Em
D
C
B

Em
C
Em
C

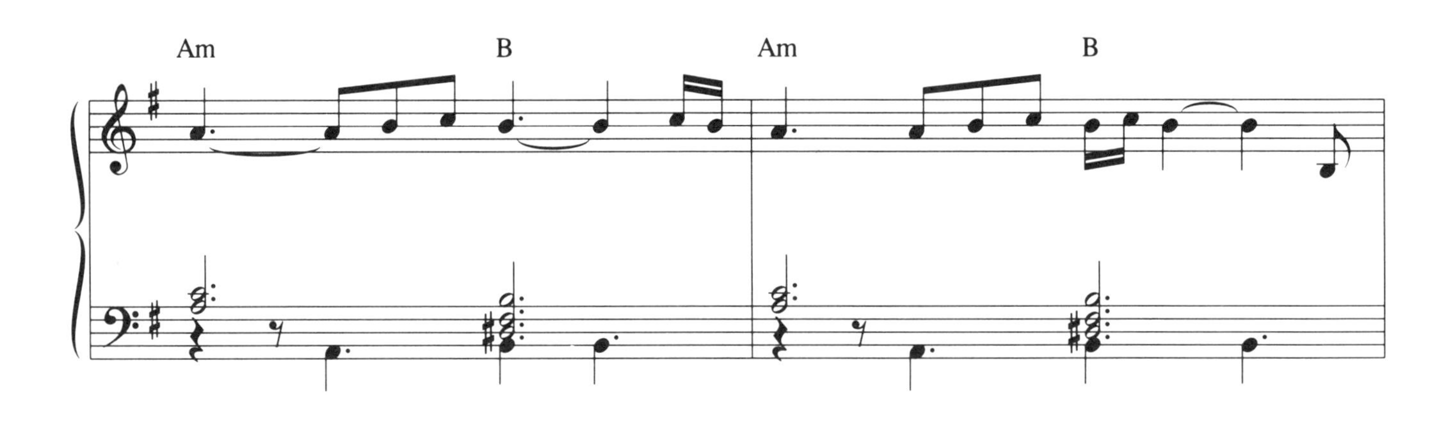
Am
B
Am
B

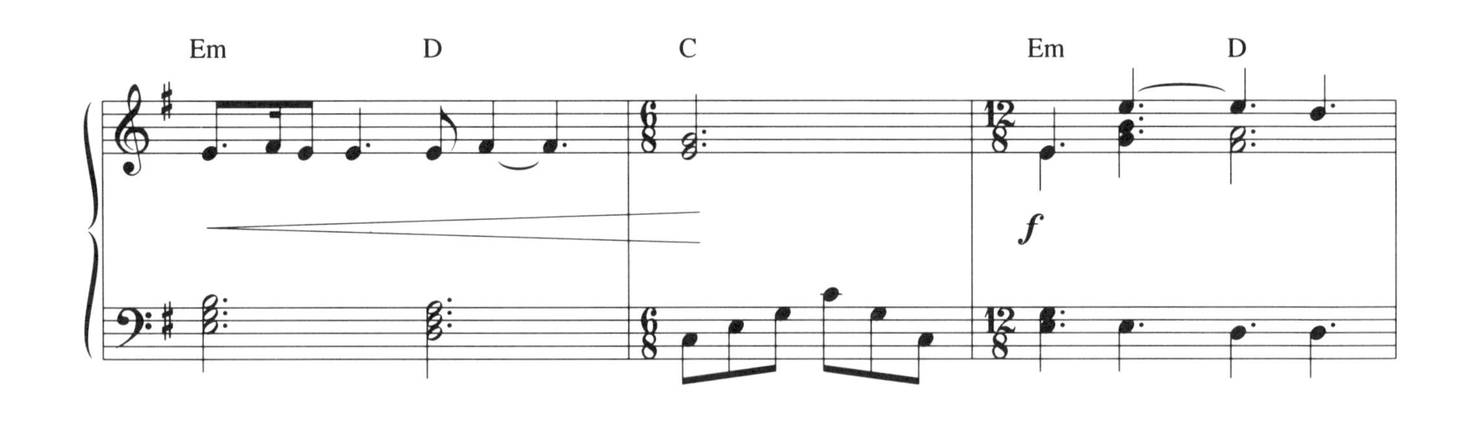
Em
D
C
Em
D
f

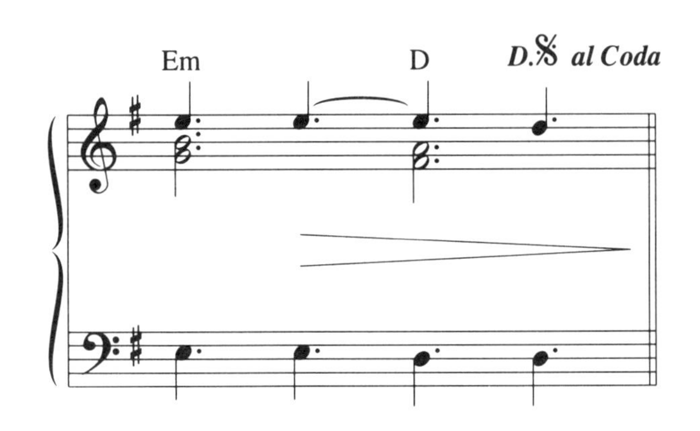
Em
D
D.𝄋 al Coda

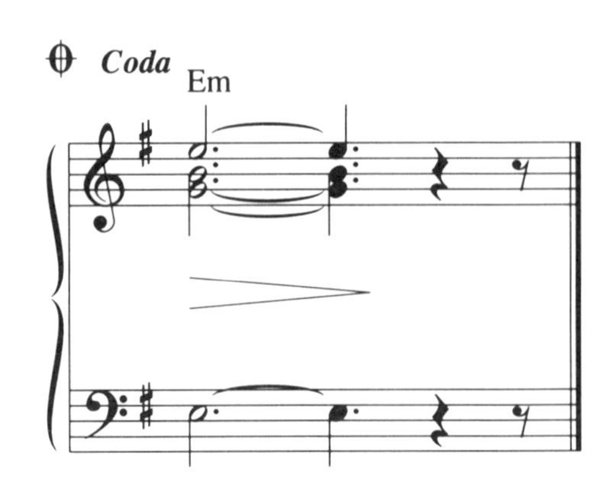
Coda
Em

Take My Breath Away

Words by Tom Whitlock
Music by Giorgio Moroder

Moderately slow

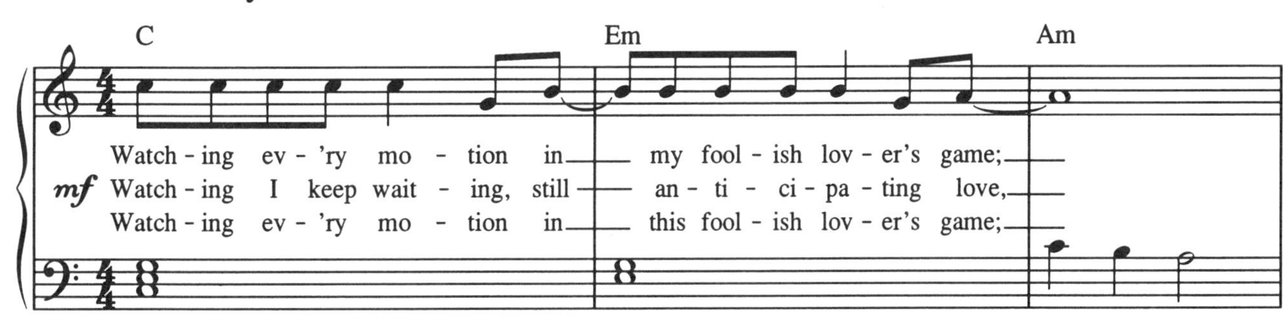

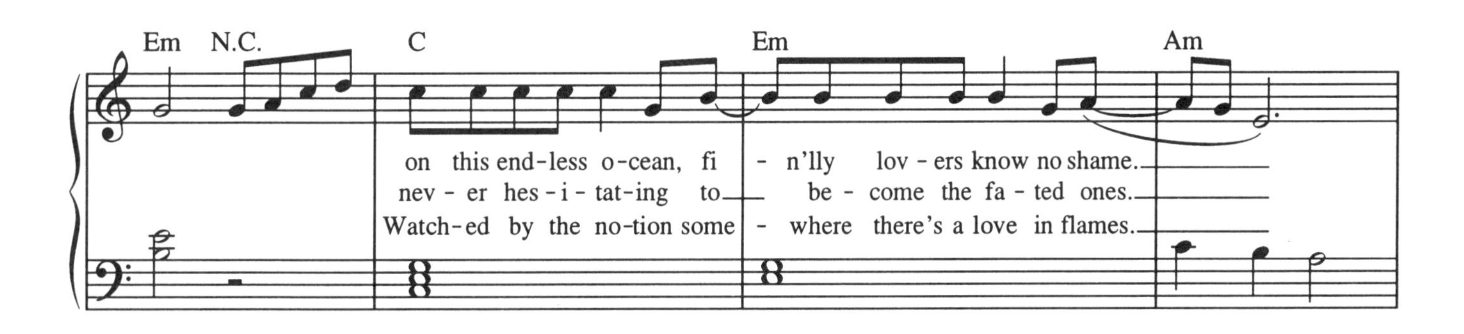

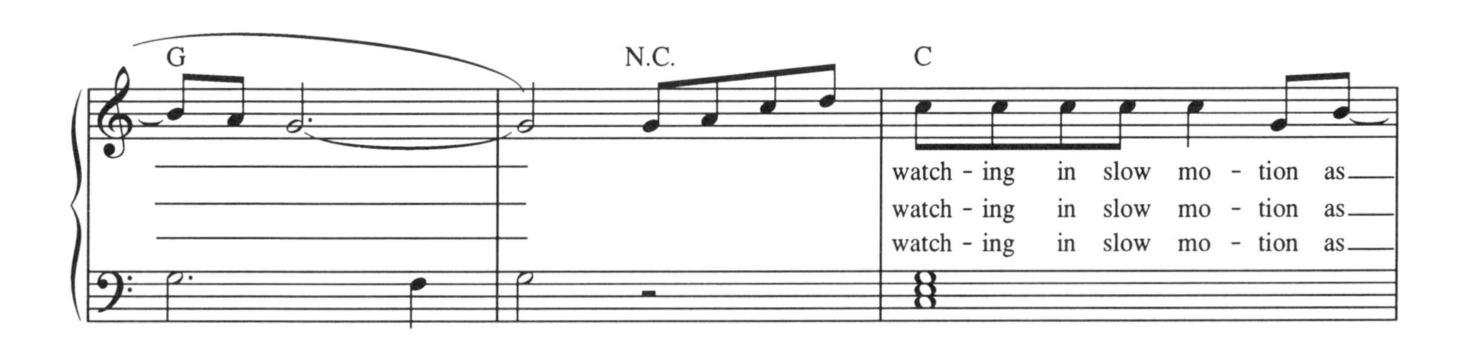

Em
F
G
N.C.
— you turn a-round and say,——
— you turn a-round and say,——
— you turn a-round and say,——
"Take my breath a-

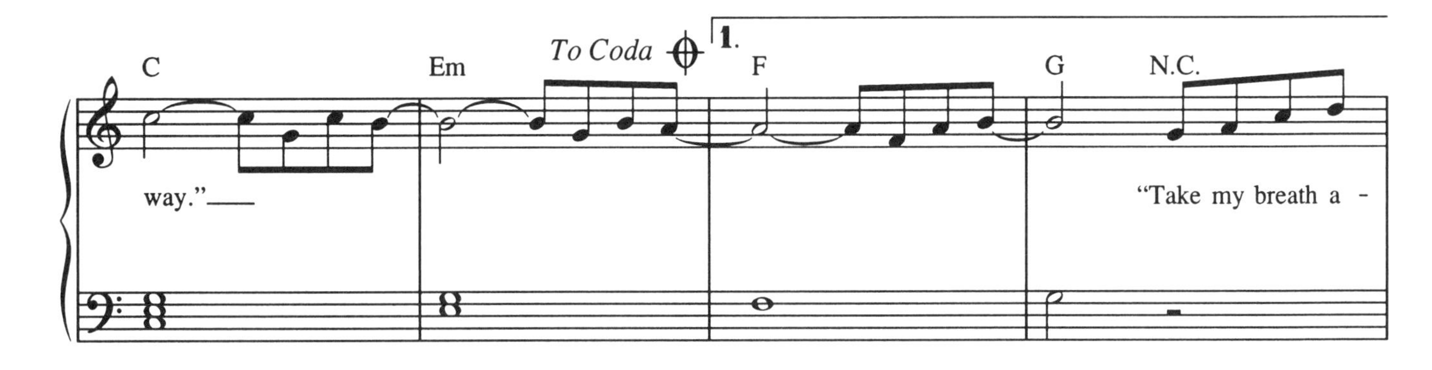
To Coda
1.
C
Em
F
G
N.C.
way."——
"Take my breath a-

C
Em
F
G
N.C.
way."——

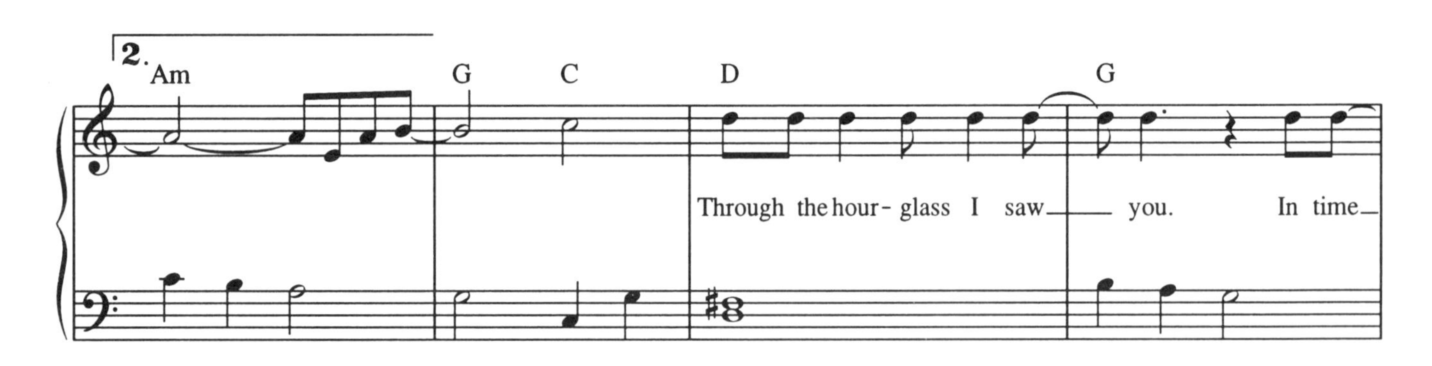
2.
Am
G
C
D
G
Through the hour-glass I saw—— you. In time—

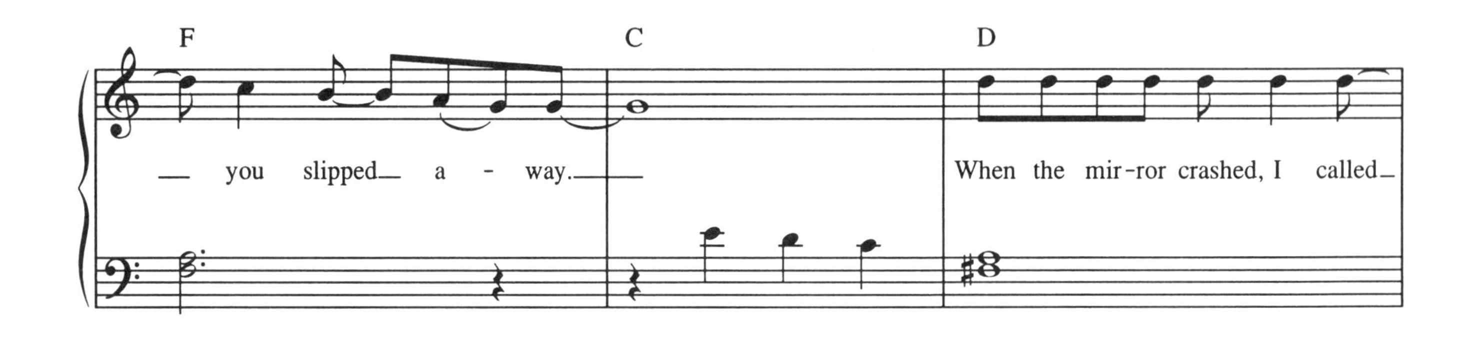
F
C
D
— you slipped— a - way.——
When the mir-ror crashed, I called—

G F C D
— you and turned — to hear — you say, — "If on - ly for to - day —
G N.C. C
— I am — un - a - fraid. — Take my breath a - way". —
1. 2. D.C. al Coda
Em Am Em N.C. Em N.C.
"Take my breath a -
CODA
F G N.C. C
My love, — Take my breath a - way. —
Em F G N.C. C
My love, — take my breath a - way.

That Ole Devil Called Love

Words & Music by Doris Fisher & Allan Roberts

Dm7 G7 D♭7(+5) C7 F B♭7
still have the rain, Still have those tears and those rocks in my heart.

F Gm7 C7 Am7 D7+
Sup-pose I did-n't stay, ran a-way, would-n't play, that

Gm7 C7 F6 Em7 A7
dev-il what a po-tion he would brew. He'd fol-low me a-round,

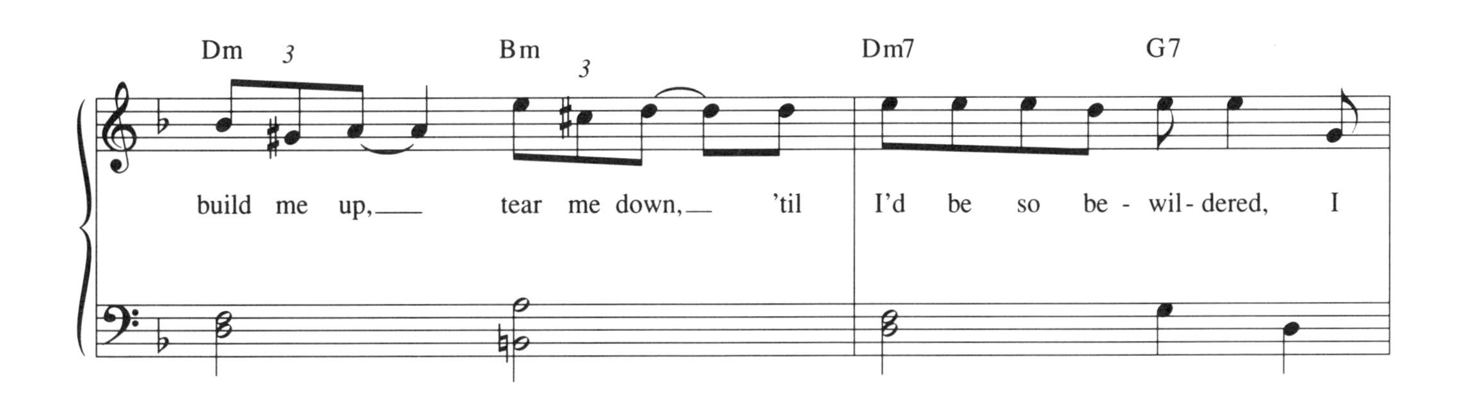
Dm Bm Dm7 G7
build me up, tear me down, 'til I'd be so be-wil-dered, I

Gm7 C7 Gm7 C7 Gm7 C7
3
would - n't know what to do. Might as well give up the fight a - gain, I know

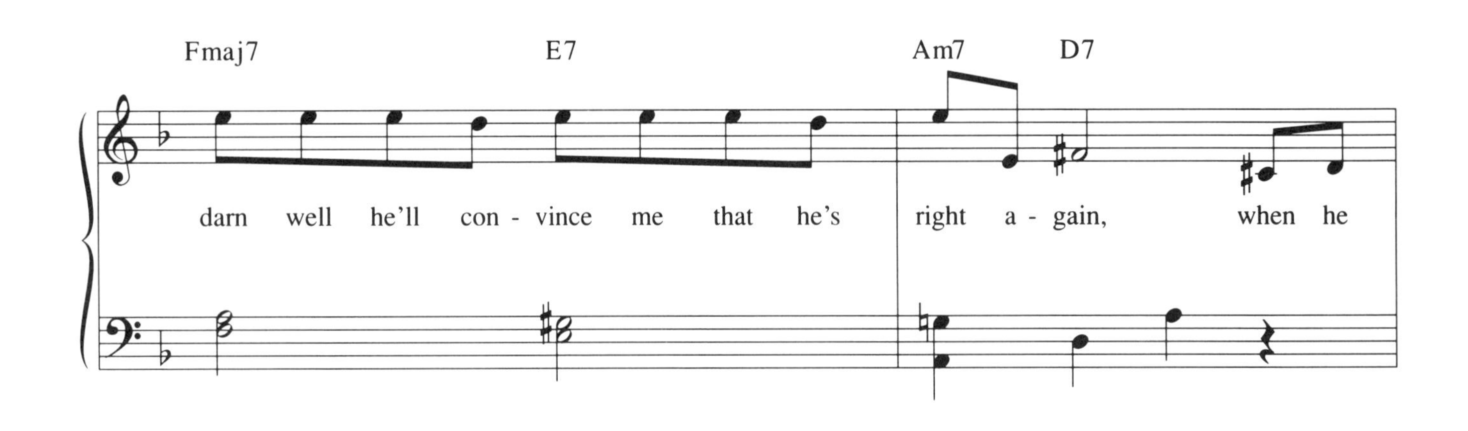
Fmaj7 E7 Am7 D7
darn well he'll con - vince me that he's right a - gain, when he

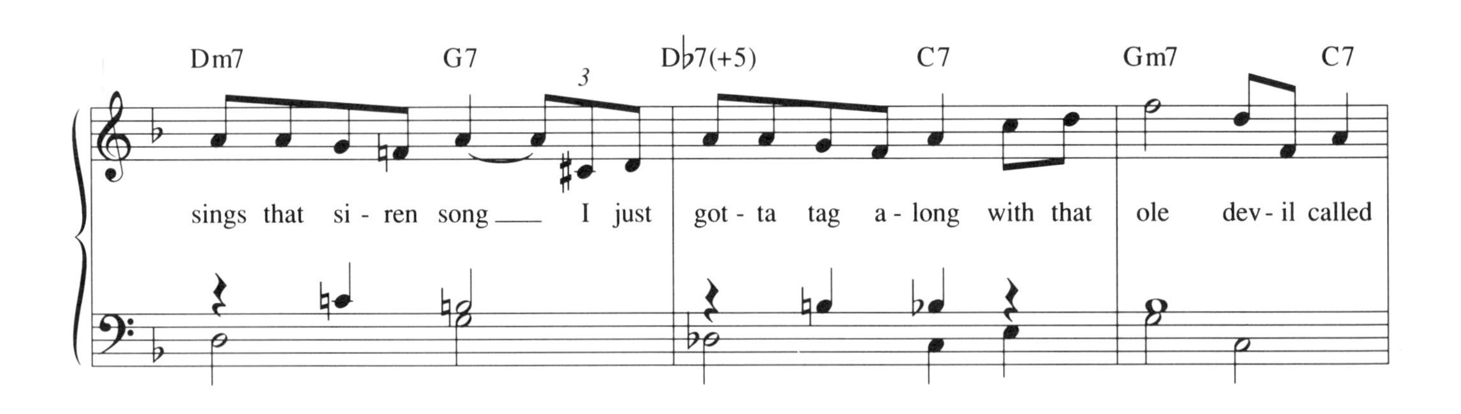
Dm7 G7 D♭7(+5) C7 Gm7 C7
3
sings that si - ren song I just got - ta tag a - long with that ole dev - il called

1.
F
love. It's that
2.
F
love.

Time To Say Goodbye

Words & Music by Franco Sartori & Lucio Quarantotto
English Translation by Frank Peterson

Moderately

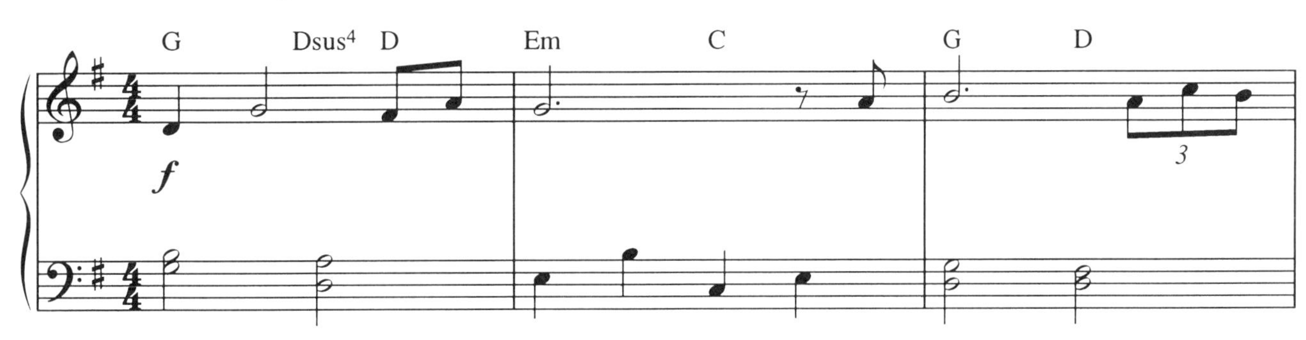

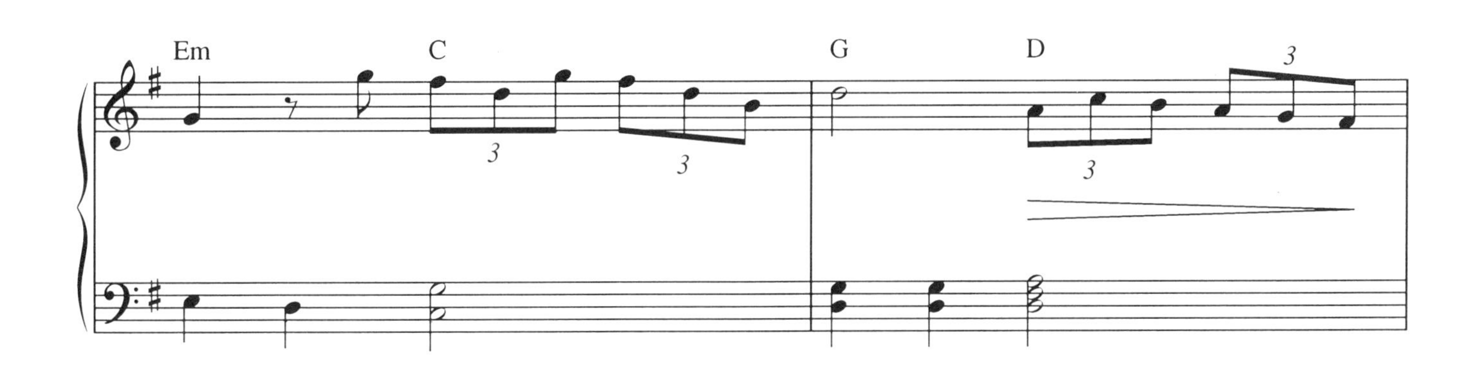

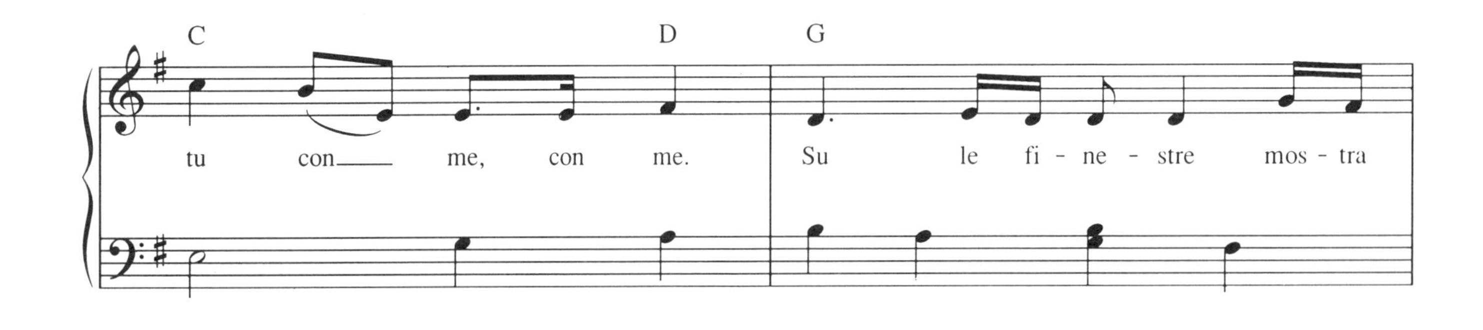
C D G
tu con me, con me. Su le fi - ne - stre mos - tra

Em7 C D G C D
tut-ti il mio du-ore che hai ac ce-so. Chiu - di - den-tro me la lu-ce che hai con-tra-to per stra-da.

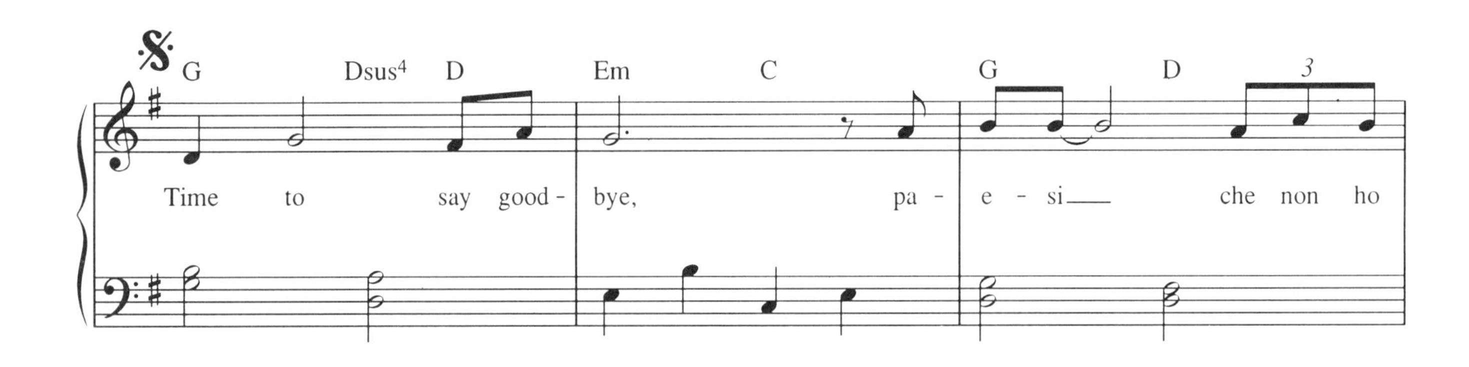
G Dsus4 D Em C G D
Time to say good - bye, pa - e - si che non ho

Em C G D
mai, ve - du - to vis - su to con me, a - des - so si, li vi -

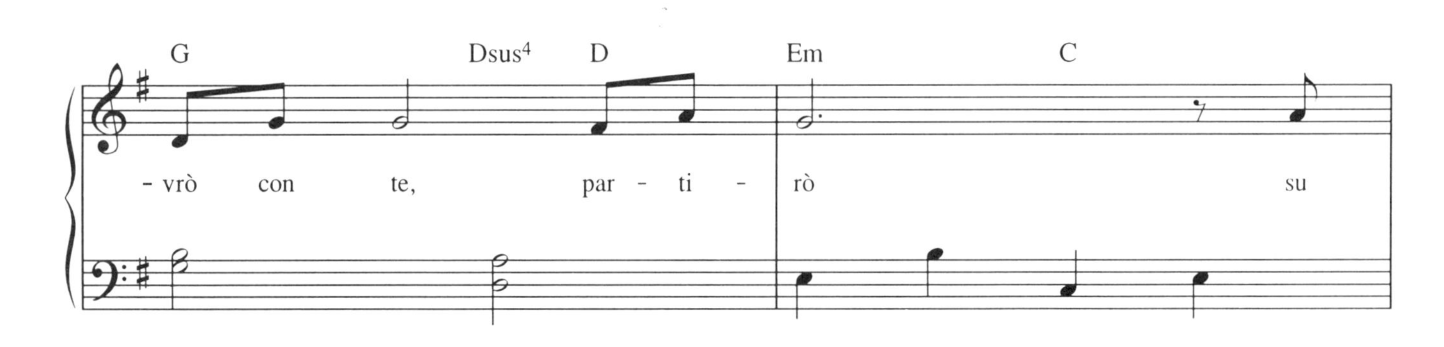
G Dsus4 D Em C
- vrò con te, par - ti - rò su

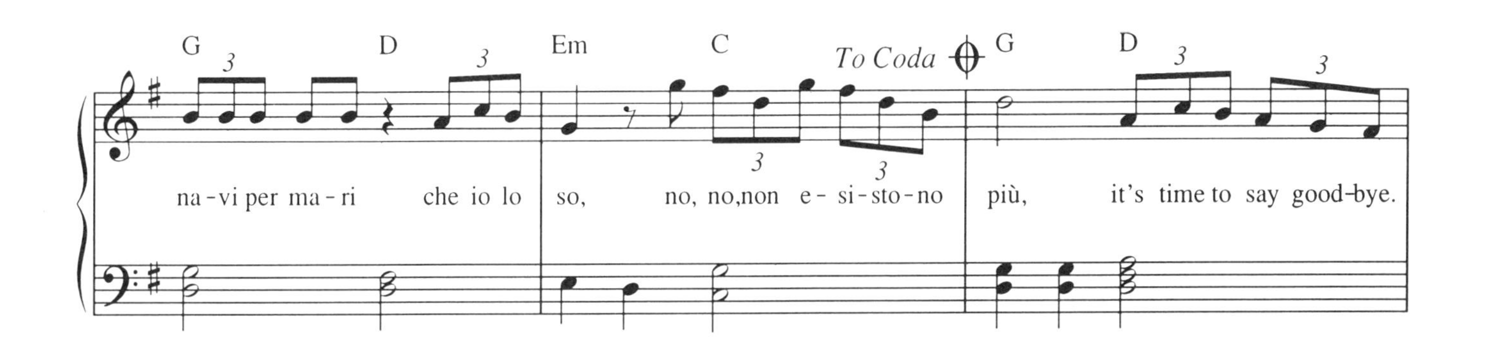
G D Em C To Coda G D
na-vi per ma-ri che io lo so, no, no,non e-si-sto-no più, it's time to say good-bye.

C/D Gsus4 G
Quan-do sei lon-ta-na sog-no l'o-riz-zon-te man-can le pa-ro-le.

C D G C
E io si, lo so che sei con me, con me, tu mia lu-na, tu sei qui con me,

D.S. al Coda
C D7 Gsus4 G D
mi-o so-le tu sei qui con me, con me, con me, con me.

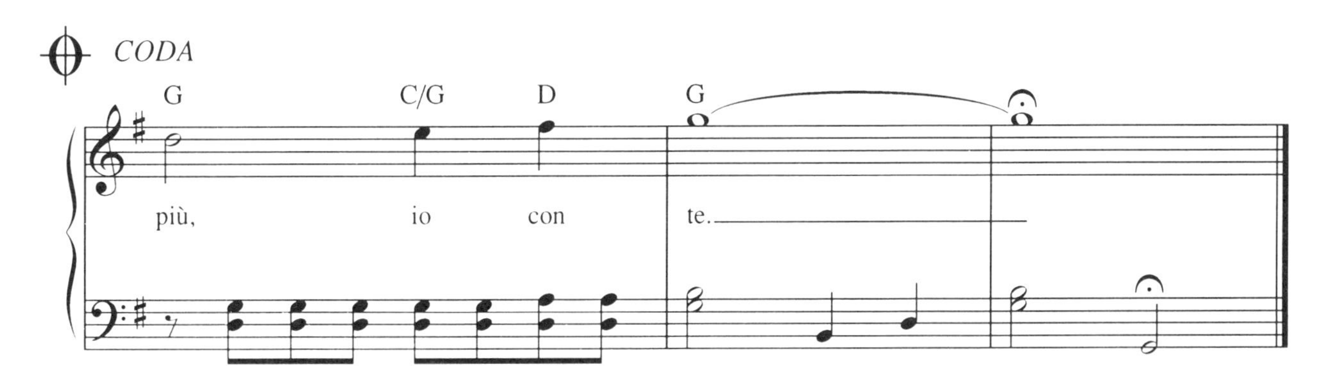
CODA
G C/G D G
più, io con te.

Try A Little Tenderness

Words & Music by Harry Woods, Jimmy Campbell & Reg Connelly

Moderately

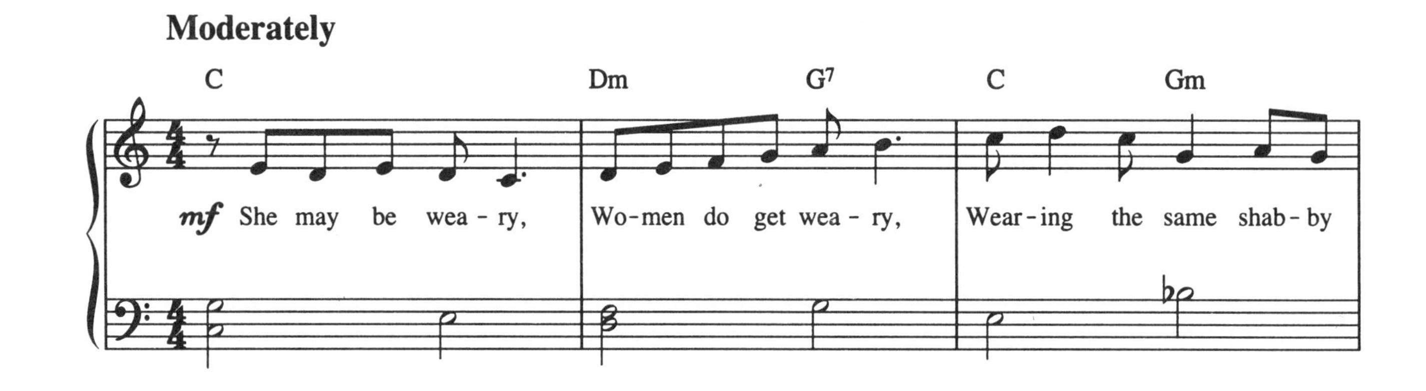

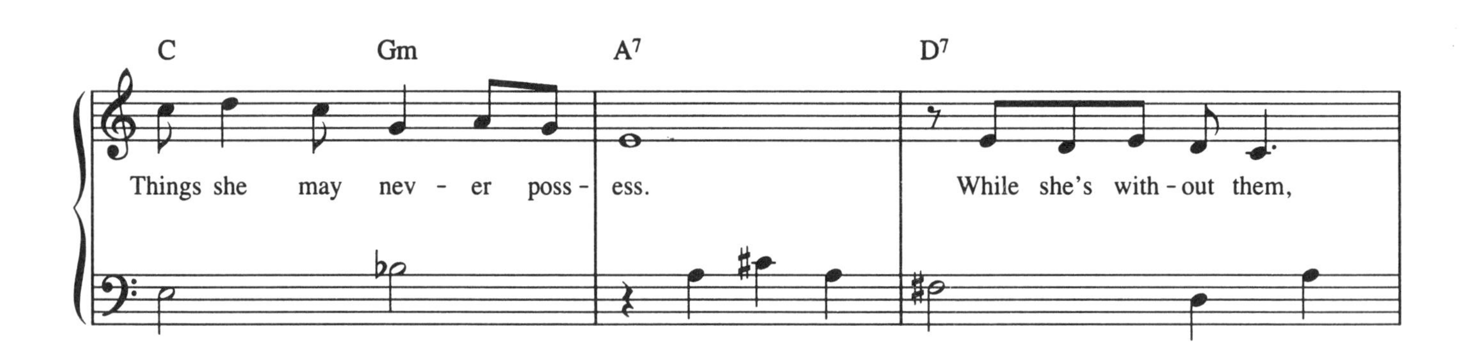

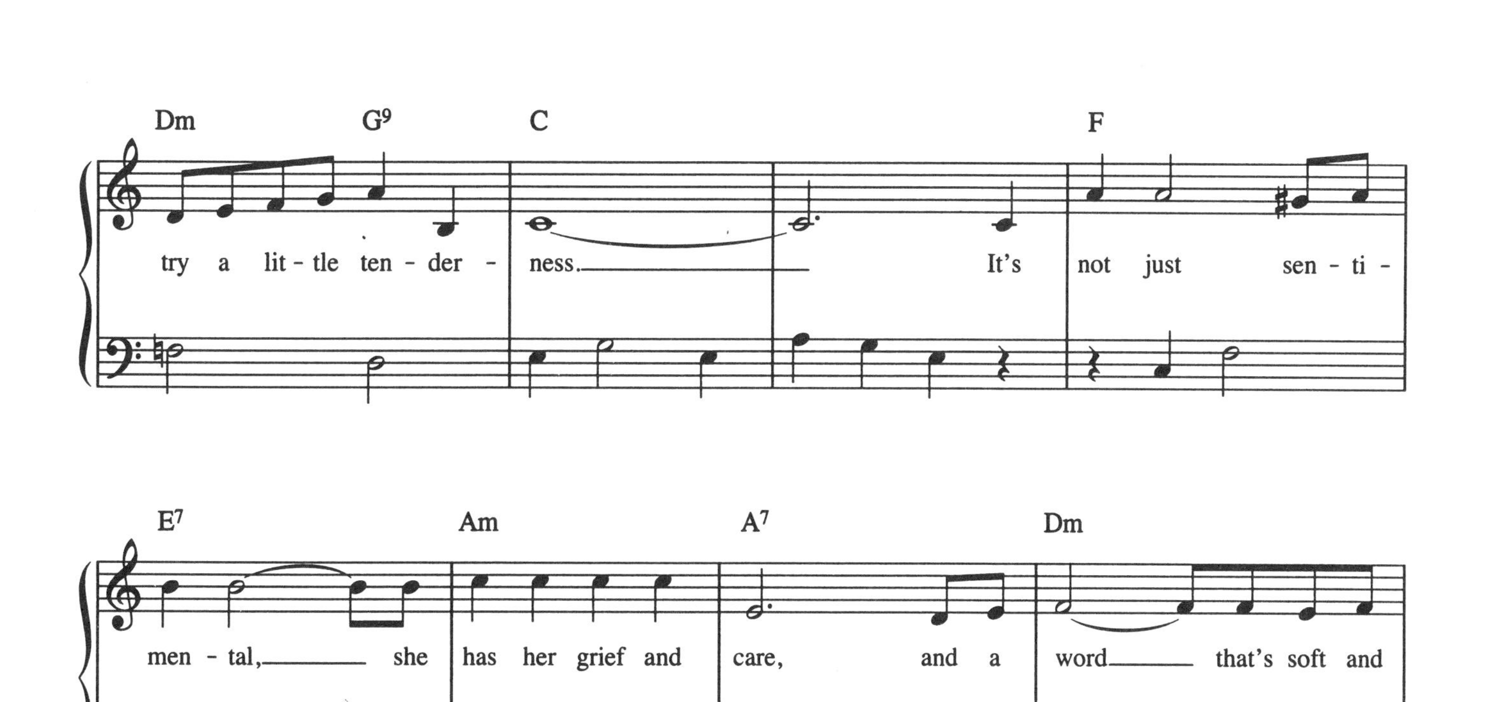
Dm G9 C F
try a lit-tle ten-der-ness. It's not just sen-ti-
E7 Am A7 Dm
men-tal, she has her grief and care, and a word that's soft and

A7 Dm7 G7 C
gen-tle, makes it ea-si-er to bear. You won't re-gret it,

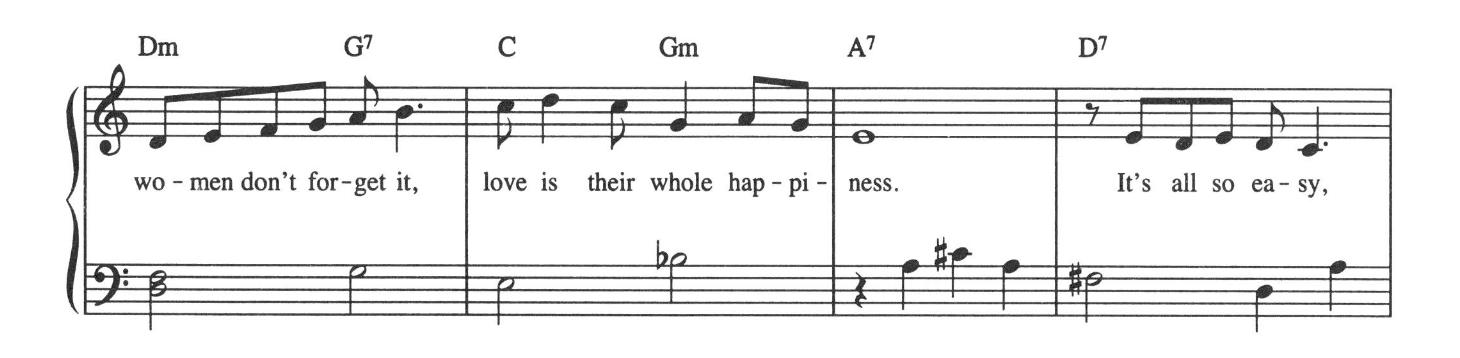
Dm G7 C Gm A7 D7
wo-men don't for-get it, love is their whole hap-pi-ness. It's all so ea-sy,

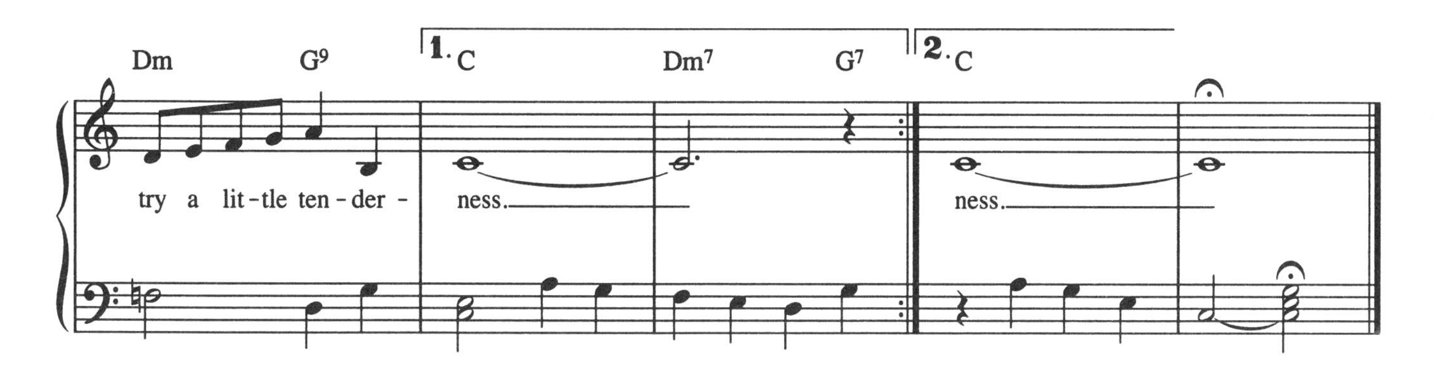
Dm G9 1. C Dm7 G7 2. C
try a lit-tle ten-der-ness. ness.

Unchained Melody

Words by Hy Zaret
Music by Alex North

Moderately slow

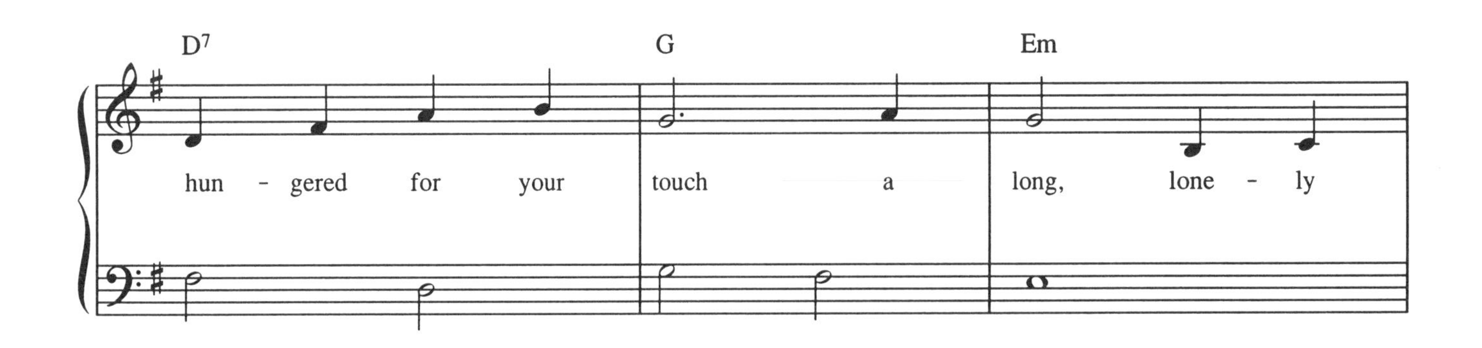

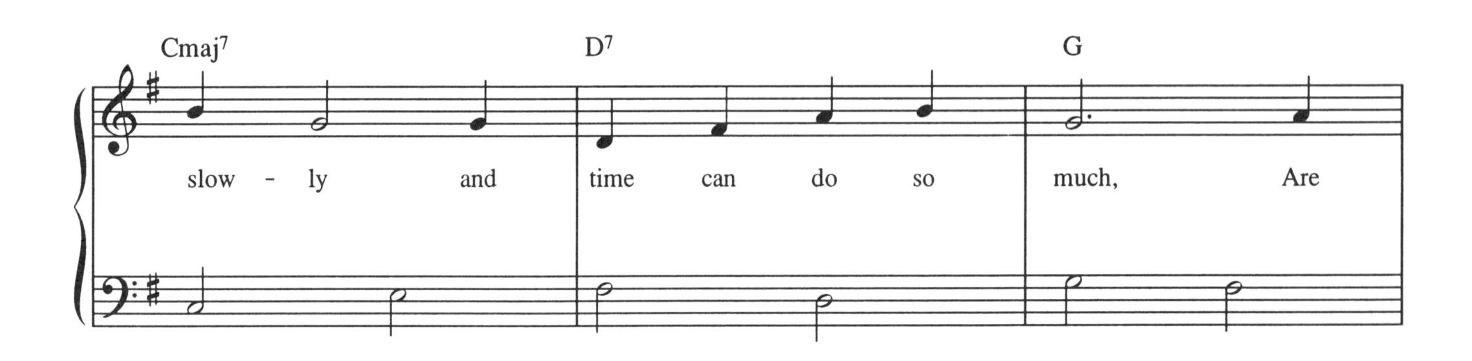

Em
Bm
D
G
you still mine? I need your love,
D
Em
Gmaj7
To Coda
I need your love, God
Am7
D7
G
speed your love to me!
C
D
C
3
1. Lone - ly ri - vers flow to the sea, to the
2. Lone - ly moun - tains gaze at the stars, at the
B♭
C
D7
sea, To the op - en arms of the
stars, Wait - ing for the dawn of the

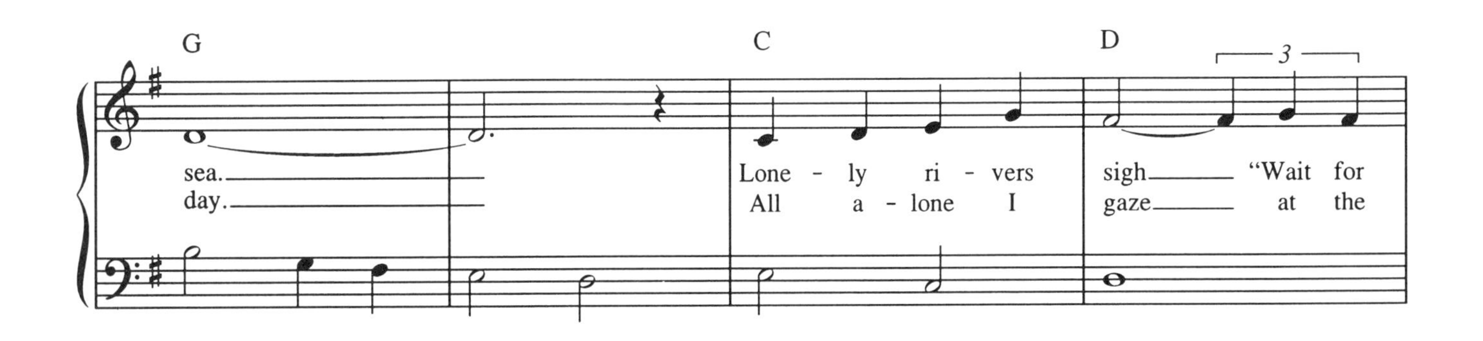
G
C
D
3
sea.
day.
Lone - ly ri - vers
All a - lone I
sigh "Wait for
gaze at the

C
B♭
C
D7
3
3
me, wait for
stars, at the
me"
stars,
I'll be com - ing
Dream - ing of my
home, wait for
love far a -

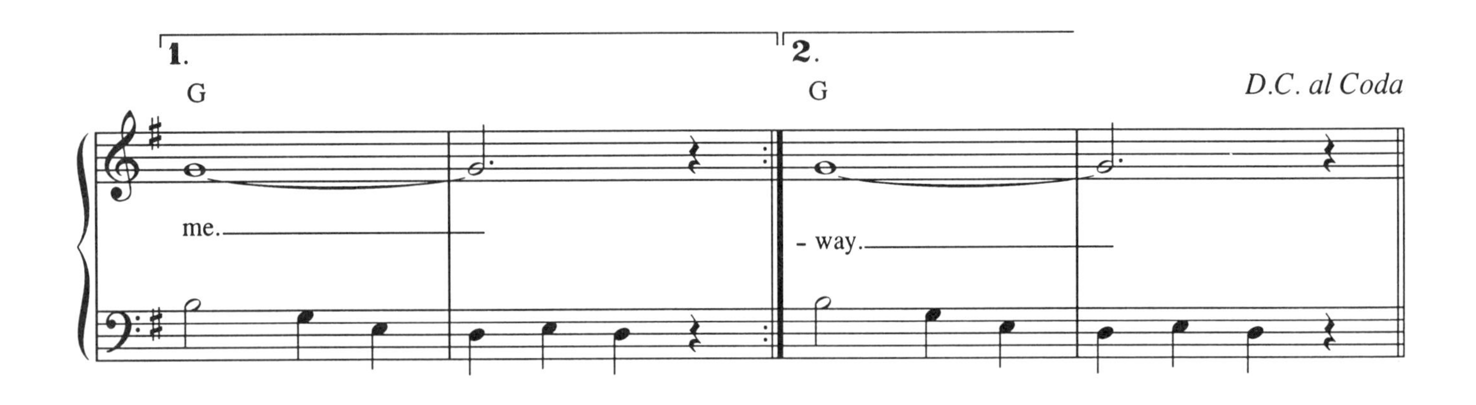
1.
2.
G
G
D.C. al Coda
me.
- way.

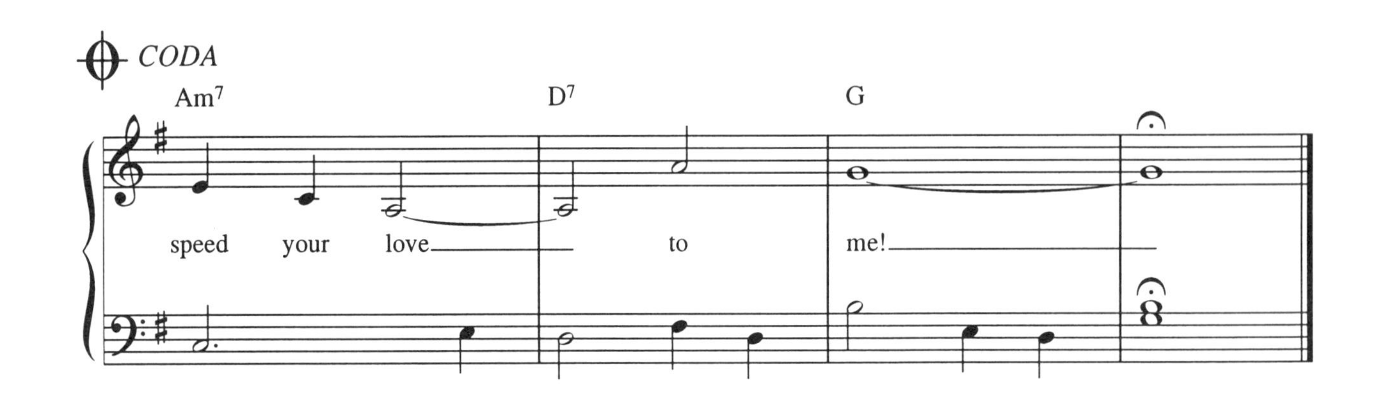
CODA
Am7
D7
G
speed your love to
me!

Wonderful Tonight

Words & Music by Eric Clapton

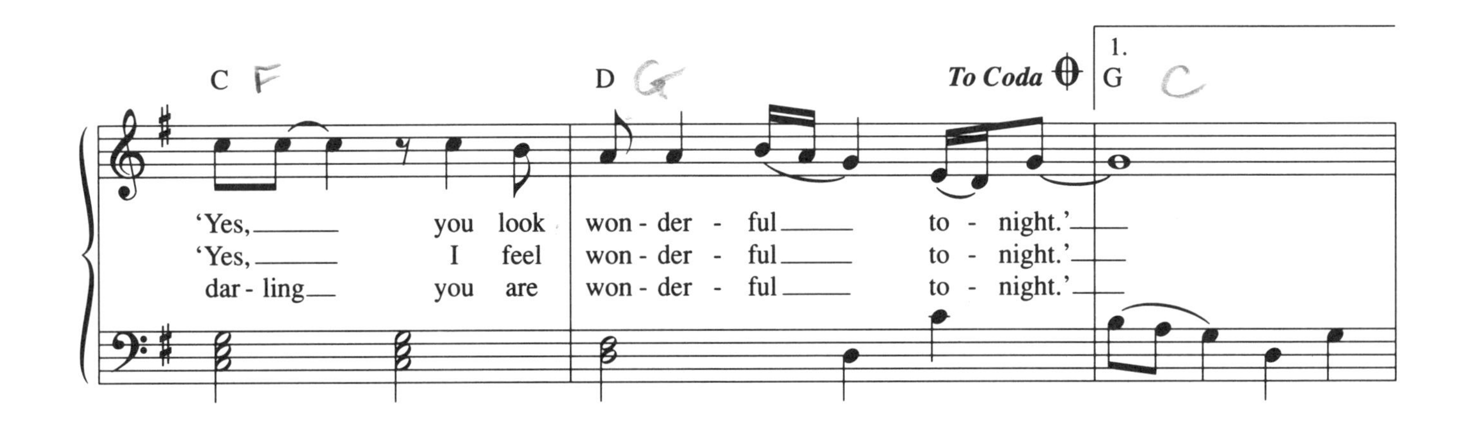
C F
D G
To Coda
1.
G C
'Yes, you look won - der - ful to - night.'
'Yes, I feel won - der - ful to - night.'
dar - ling you are won - der - ful to - night.'

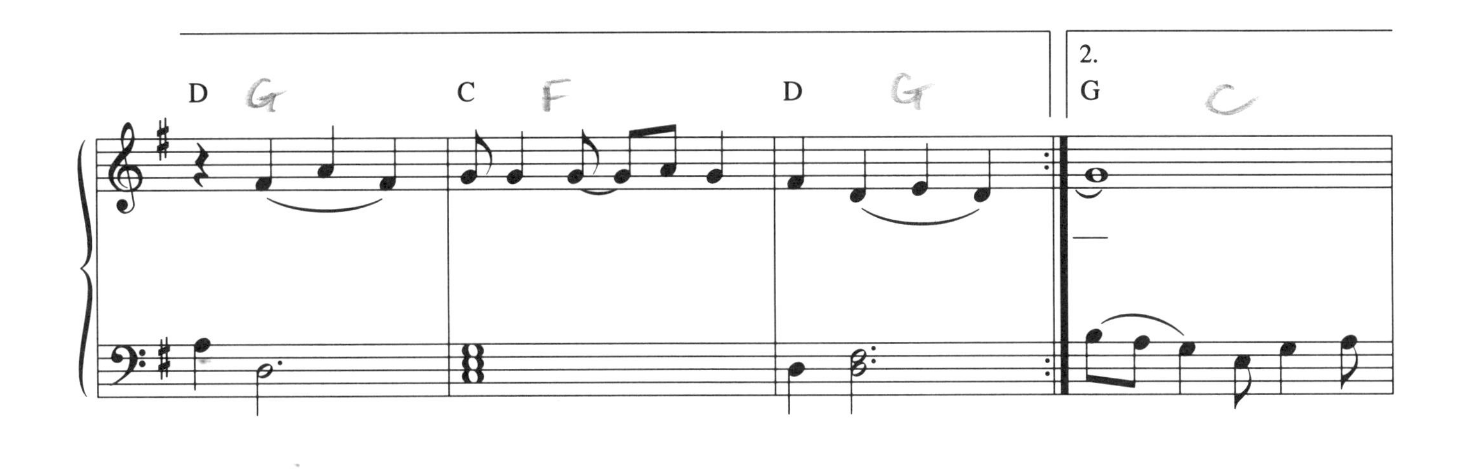
D G
C F
D G
2.
G C

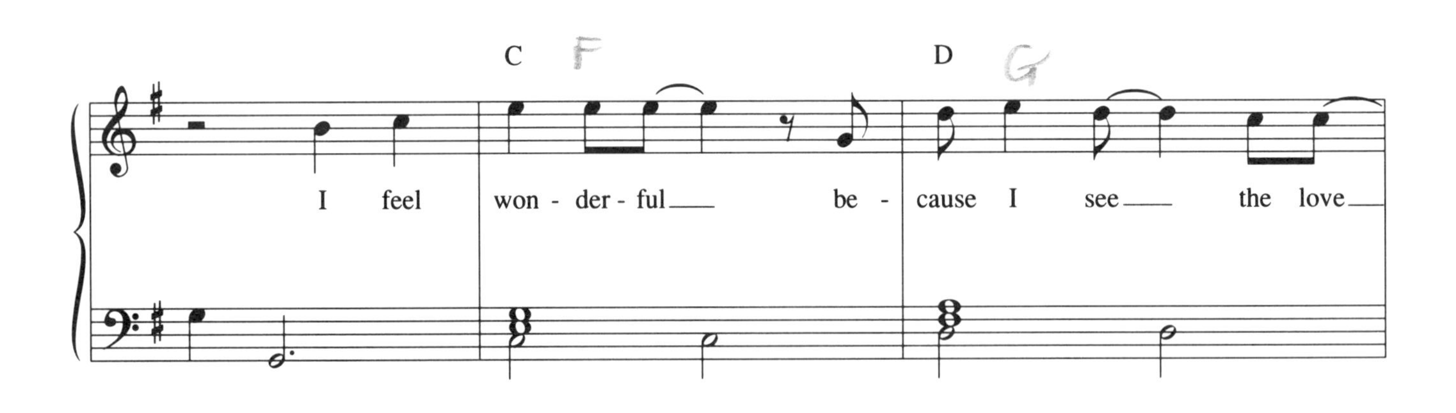
C F
D G
I feel won - der - ful be - cause I see the love

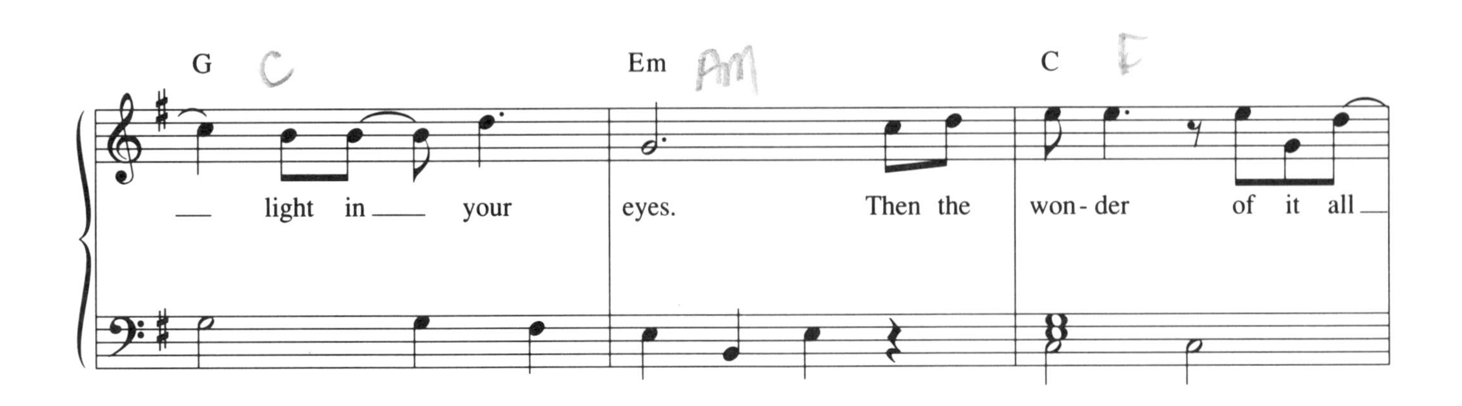
G C
Em Am
C F
light in your eyes. Then the won - der of it all

D
C
D
is that you just don't re - al - ise how much I

G
D
C
D
D.C. al Coda
love you.
(No repeat on vocal)

CODA
G
Em
C
Oh my dar- ling, you are

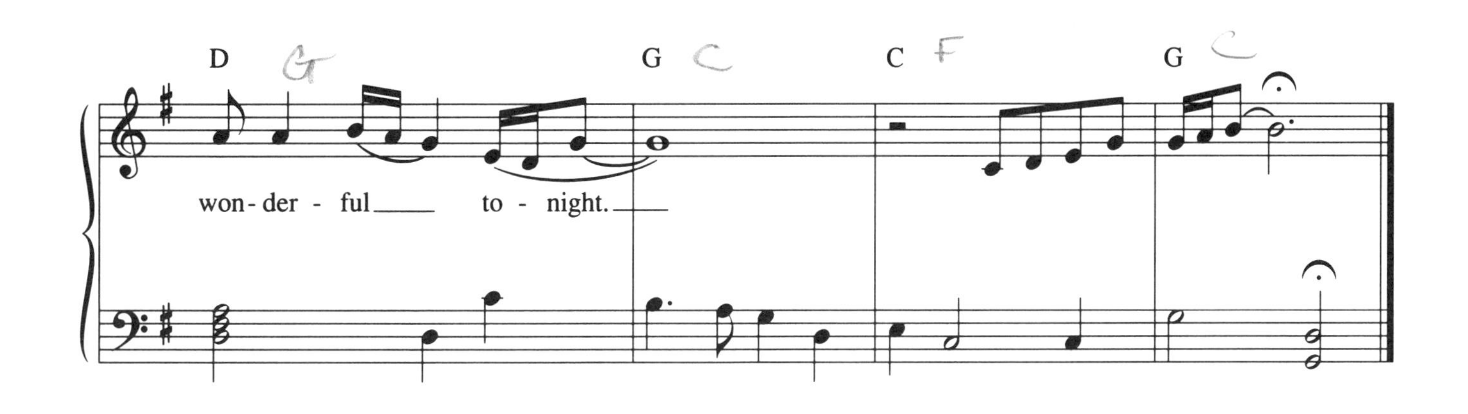
D
G
C
G
won- der - ful to - night.

A Whiter Shade Of Pale

Words & Music by Keith Reid & Gary Brooker

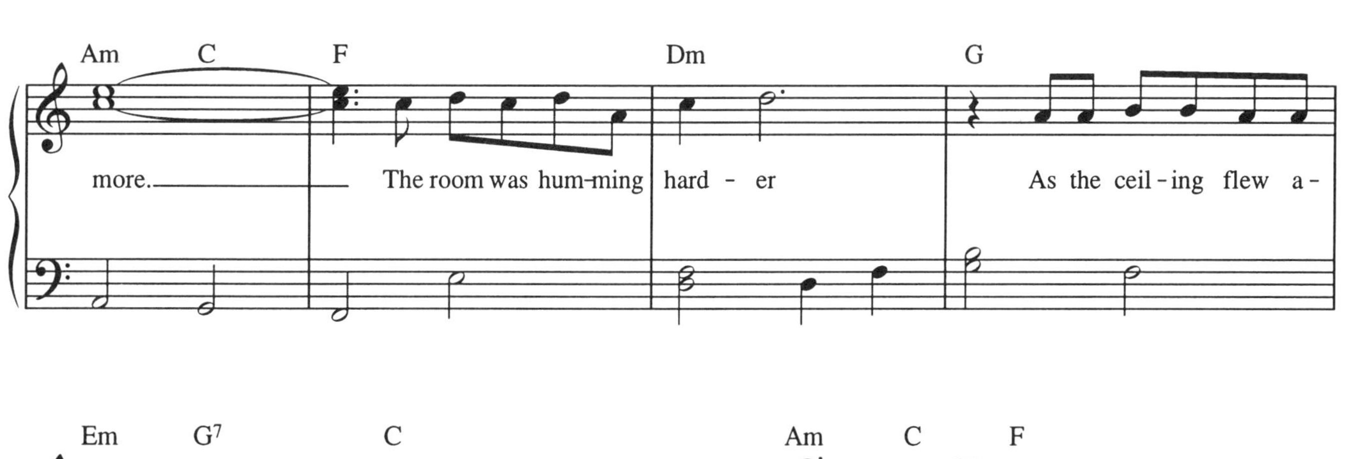
Am C F Dm G
more. The room was hum-ming hard - er As the ceil - ing flew a -

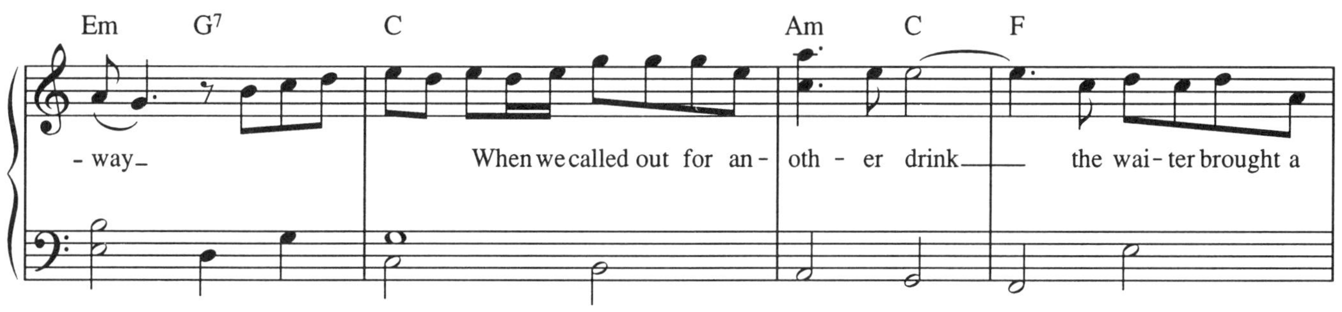
Em G7 C Am C F
- way When we called out for an - oth - er drink the wai - ter brought a

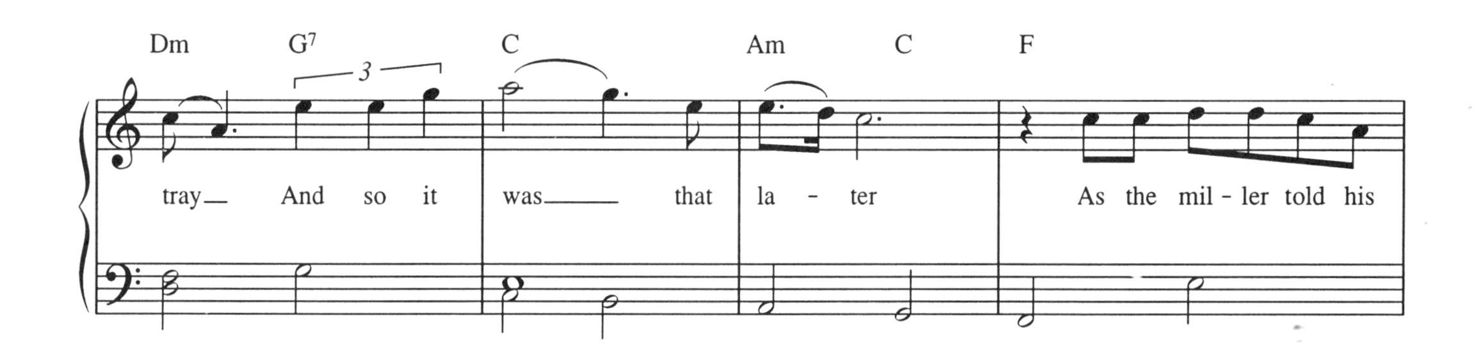
Dm G7 C Am C F
3
tray And so it was that la - ter As the mil - ler told his

Dm G7 Em G Am/G
tale That her face at first just ghost - ly Turned a

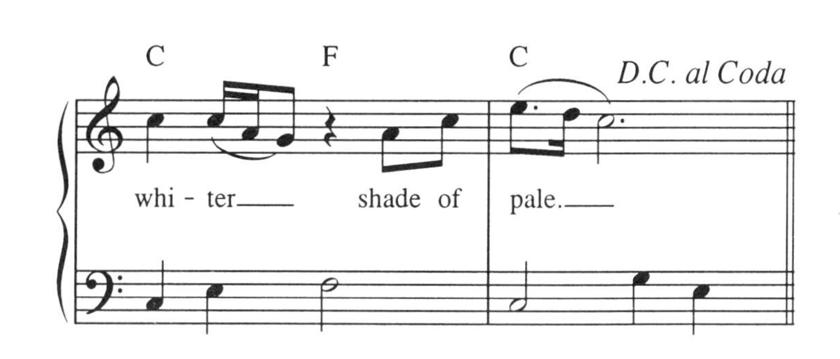
C F C
D.C. al Coda
whi - ter shade of pale.

CODA
C G7 C

You're The One That I Want

Words & Music by John Farrar

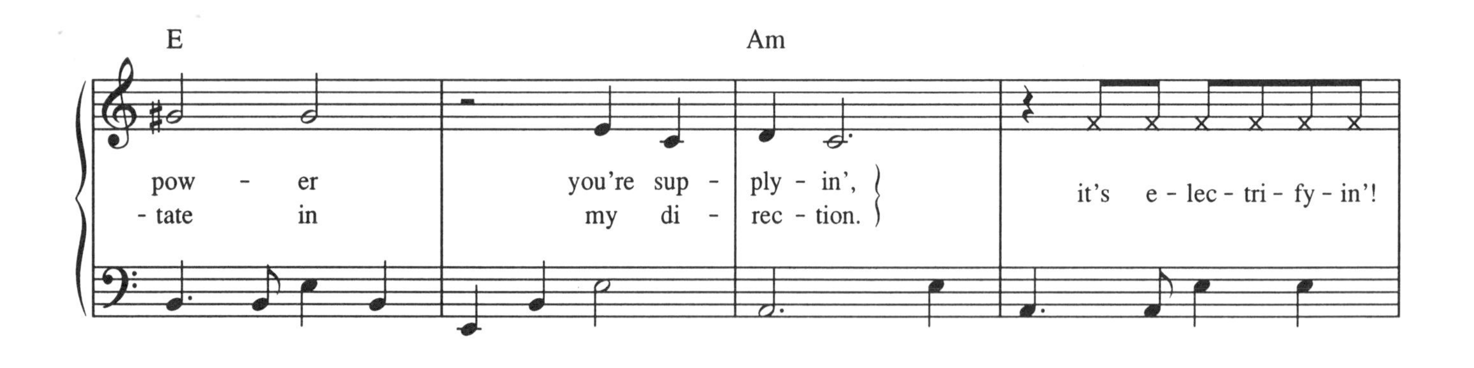

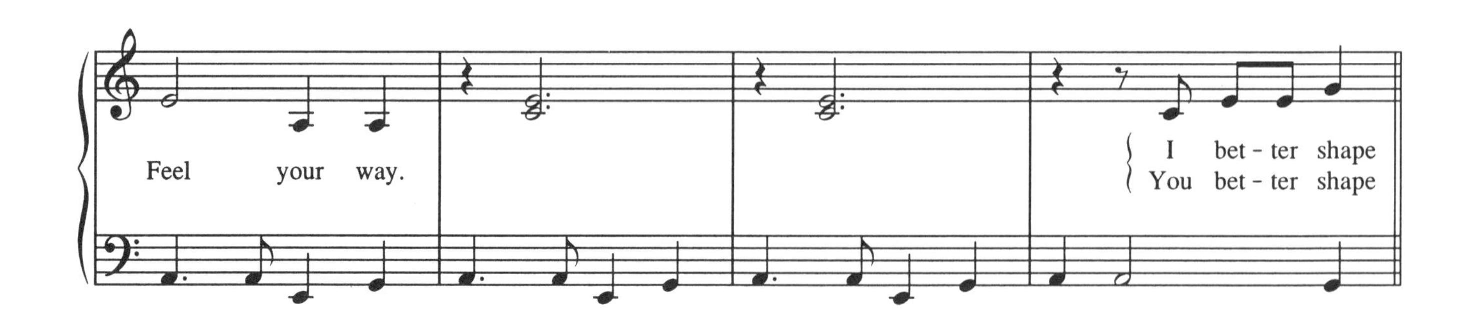

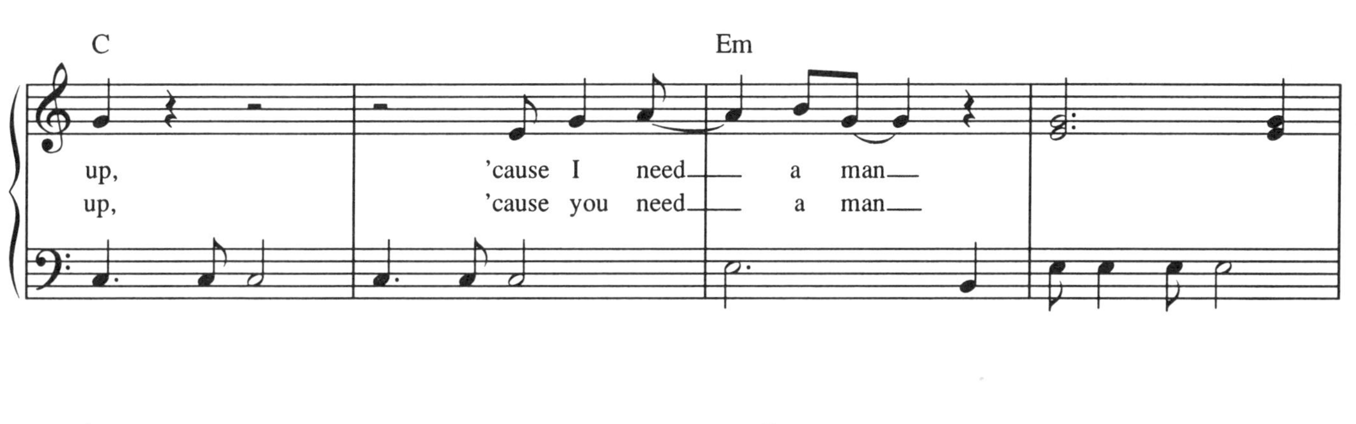
C
Em
up,
'cause I need a man
up,
'cause you need a man

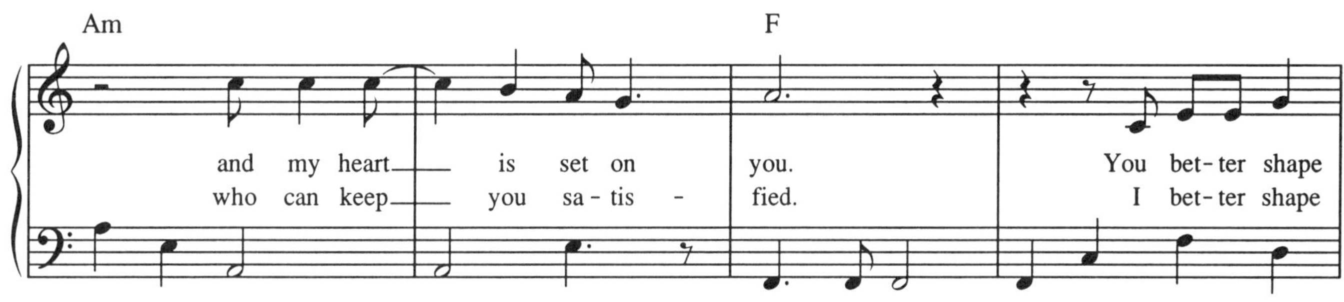
Am
F
and my heart is set on you.
You bet-ter shape
who can keep you sa-tis - fied.
I bet-ter shape

C
Em
up,
you bet - ter un - der - stand
up,
if I'm gon - na prove

Am
F
to my heart I must be true.
Noth - in'
that your faith is jus - ti - fied.
Are you

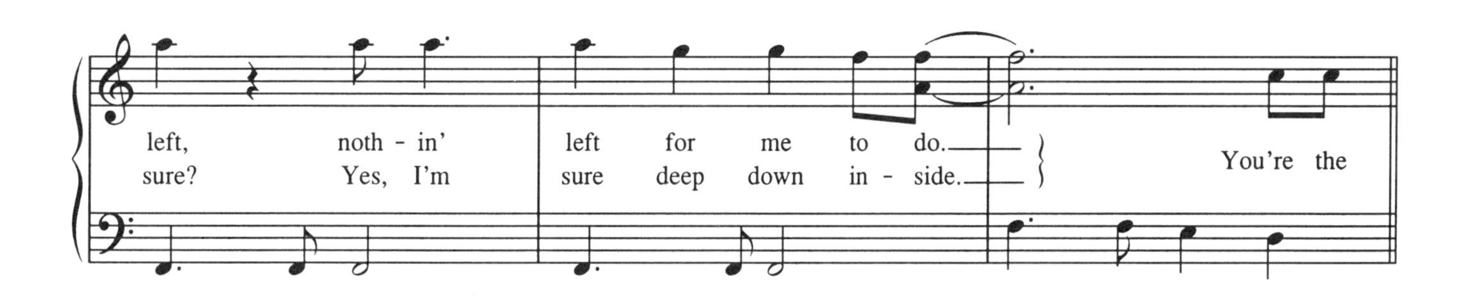
left, noth - in' left for me to do.
sure? Yes, I'm sure deep down in - side.
You're the

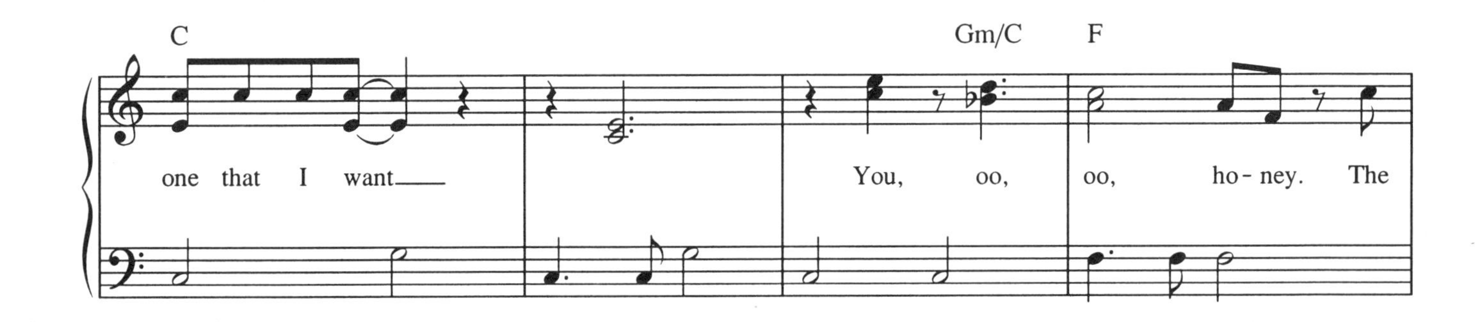

Printed in Malta by Progress Press Co. Ltd 11/06 (60263)